Bariatric Air fryer Cookbook

Easy-to-Follow Nutritional and Deliciously Fried Recipes to Help You Keep the Weight Off for Every Stage of the Post Surgery Recovery

By

Carrie Shawn

Table of Contents

INTRODUCTION

Bariatric surgery is a procedure that aims to assist a patient in losing weight. This method is typically indicated for individuals who need to lose a significant amount of weight for health reasons but have been unable to do so despite adopting dietary and lifestyle modifications such as exercising.

There are different types of bariatric surgical procedures that can be used to aid weight loss in patients namely: sleeve gastrectomy, gastric bypass, gastric balloon, gastric banding biliopancreatic diversion (either with or without a duodenal switch). These procedures either reduce and shorten the stomach. Consequently, people feel full considerably faster (fewer calories intake), feel less hungry due to hormonal changes as a result of lower hunger hormone secretion.

On average, patients lose about 50 percent of their extra weight within 18-24 months. Some people lose as much as 60-70 percent of their body weight.
However, to obtain long-term results after bariatric surgery, patients are expected to adhere to long-term follow-up plans that include monitoring their nutrition, lifestyle, and behavior.

The Air Fryer appliance makes the switch to a healthier life is more achievable by delivering healthier fried meals and foods by eliminating the calories associated with fried foods while maintaining the crunchiness, texture, and quality that you enjoy.
This cookbook does not only contain tasty and easy-to-follow air fryer recipes, but also enlightens you on the bariatric diet, pre-op and post-op diet tips, and phases.

CHAPTER 1: Introduction to the Bariatric Diet

1.1 What is Bariatric Diet

This is a diet that a person who is planning or has had bariatric surgery must rigorously adhere to. It helps the body to heal faster and acclimate to a smaller stomach.

1.2 Pre-Op Diet Tips

You'll be given a special diet to follow for two weeks before your gastric sleeve surgery, starting two weeks before your scheduled operation date. This will help to reduce the accumulation of fat in and around the liver which could pose a challenge to a surgery.

You will eat primarily lean protein, vegetables, and low- or no-calorie fluids. Your doctor may give you a caloric goal to stick to daily.

You will stick to a clear, liquid diet two days prior to surgery. In addition to broth, water, decaffeinated coffee or tea, Jell-O, and sugar-free popsicles, one no-sugar protein shake per day may be included.

Caffeinated and carbonated drinks should be avoided at all costs.

1.3 Post-Op Diet and Phases

WEEK 1 DIET

For the first week after the surgery, you'll stick to the same clear liquid diet you did in the days leading up to the procedure. This can assist to avoid issues such as intestinal obstruction, gastric leakage, diarrhea, constipation, and dehydration that can occur after surgery. Ensure you drink plenty of clear fluids.

Sugar, caffeinated and carbonated beverages should be avoided after surgery and in the long term.

WEEK 2 DIET

Two weeks post-surgery you will advance to a full-liquid diet. To begin, make the majority of your meals high-protein and low-sugar shakes. Protein powders mixed with liquid, sugar-free ice cream, oatmeal, sugarless beverages, creamy soups, non-fat yogurts, soupy noodles, and sugar-free pudding are some of the items you can eat at this time. Carbonated beverages and caffeine should be avoided. You may notice an increase in your appetite at this time. That is entirely natural, but it is not an excuse to consume solid foods.

WEEK 3 DIET

Third week after the surgery, soft, pureed foods are gradually introduced to your diet. Any low-fat, sugar-free food that can be pureed is suitable, including lean protein sources and nonfibrous vegetables. Example of foods you can eat at this stage include: Soup, cottage cheese, low fat, diced tuna or chicken, canned chicken, turkey meatloaf and turkey chili, scrambled eggs, tuna and salmon mixed with light mayo, steamed carrots, mashed potato, oatmeal, fat-free plain greek yogurt, protein shakes blended with yogurt and nonfat milk. you chew your food slowly and thoroughly. Alcohol, caffeine, carbonated and sugary beverages should still be avoided.

WEEK 4 DIET

At one-month post-surgery, solid foods are reintroduced into your diet. Remember your stomach is still sensitive, it's important that you eat slowly and chew thoroughly. During this time, protein shakes should still be consumed in order to achieve your daily protein goal. Foods you can eat at this stage include well-cooked chicken and fish, well-cooked vegetables, sweet potatoes, low-fat cheese, fruit, low-sugar cereal.

Food you have to avoid during this stage are: breads, desserts, dried fruits, popcorn, nuts, granola, seeds, stringy or fibrous vegetables, such as celery, broccoli, corn or cabbage, sodas and carbonated beverages.

WEEK 5 DIET

At this stage you can eat solid food securely. It's time to put your new-normal eating plan into action on a long-term basis. Your diet should be focused on lean protein and vegetables, introducing one new food at a time to monitor your body's reaction. Sugary foods and soda should be avoided totally or consumed only on rare occasions from now on. All other foods can be reintroduced unless they cause symptoms. Pick nutrient-dense foods and stay away from empty calories when eating. Sticking to your plan may be easier if you eat three small meals a day and have few snacks.

Remember to always stay hydrated, eat slowly and chew thoroughly.

CHAPTER 2: Introduction to The Air Fryer

2.1 What is an Air Fryer

An air fryer is a modern kitchen equipment that cooks food without using oil by circulating very hot air around it. It provides a low-fat substitute to foods normally cooked in a deep fryer. As a result, unhealthy meals like French fries, fried chicken, and onion rings are cooked with no oil or with up to 80% less fat than traditional cooking methods.

The Air Fryer delivers healthier fried meals and foods by eliminating the calories associated with fried foods while maintaining the crunchiness, texture, and quality that you enjoy.

An air fryer can be used for almost anything. Grilling, baking, and roasting are all options in addition to frying. Its wide range of cooking options makes it simple to prepare any type of food at any time.

2.2 How Does an Air Fryer Work

The air fryer works by coating the desired food in a thin layer of oil and applying heat and initiating the reaction with circulating air heated to 200 °C (392 °F). The heat crisps and dries the outside of the food ingredient while softening and moistening the inside.

2.3 Benefits of Using an Air Fryer

i.   **Healthier Foods and Low-Fat Meals:** The air fryer's most important feature is that it uses hot-air circulation to cook food ingredients from all angles, obviating the need for oil. This allows individuals on a low-fat diet to produce delicious and healthy meals with ease with up to 80 percent less fat. Making that switch to a healthier life is more achievable by using this appliance.

ii. **Saves Time and Energy:** Preheating conventional ovens can take fifteen to twenty minutes at times. Because the air fryer is so compact, it only takes two or three minutes to pre-heat! That's a significant time and energy savings. You don't have to heat up the entire kitchen to preheat your air fryer. Plus, there's more. Food cooks quickly in the air fryer, roughly 25% faster than in an oven, so you save time and energy there as well.

iii. **Safe and Easy to Use:** Remember how you had to be extra careful when putting chicken or other things into the deep fryer? Because the heated oil is always hot, you want to be sure it doesn't spill and burn your skin. You won't have to worry about burnt skin from hot oil spills if you use an air fryer. All of the frying is done by it, and it is absolutely safe. However, when moving your fryer, wear cooking gloves to avoid hot burns. Keep your air fryer out of the reach of children as well.

iv. **Multifunctional Purposes:** Because it can cook numerous items at once, the air fryer allows you to multitask. It's your one-stop appliance for grilling, baking, frying, and roasting your favorite recipes! You don't need numerous appliances for different tasks any longer. It can do tasks that would otherwise require the use of different equipment. It has the ability to grill meat, roast vegetables, and bake pastries. It's a great alternative to using your oven, deep fryer, or stovetop.

v. Clean and Tidy: There is no grease and thus no mess when using the Air Fryer. Because there are no oil spills on the walls or floors to clean up, and no scraping or scrubbing of pans, cleanup time is delightful. The non-stick material used in the air fryer parts prevents food from clinging to the surfaces, making it difficult to clean. Cleaning and maintaining these components are simple. They may be taken apart and cleaned in the dishwasher.

2.4 Air Fryer's Usage Tips

i. Preheat: When you haven't used your air fryer in a while, preheat it. Allow for a 3-5 minute preheating period to ensure appropriate heat distribution.

ii. Keep it Dry: Dry foods, especially marinated meals, should be patted dry before cooking. This will keep the smoke and splatter to a minimum. When foods with a high fat content, such as chicken breasts and wings, are cooked, the fat is frequently deposited. As a result, empty the collected fat from the bottom of the air fryer on a regular basis.

iii. Ensure You Spray Foods: When using your air fryer, you'll need your cooking spray to keep items from adhering to the basket. Foods can be lightly sprayed or a small amount of oil can be added.

iv. Give Enough Spacing to Your Food: When it comes to the air fryer, overcrowding is a no-no. Give your items plenty of room to cook so that air can move freely. You want your food to be crisp, right? Overcrowding makes it impossible for air to circulate over the foods. Hence, spread out your food well.

CHAPTER 3: Breakfast Recipes

1. Spinach Muffins

Prep time: 10 minutes / Cooking Time: 28 Minutes/ Total time: 38 minutes / Yield: 4 Servings.
Ingredients:
¼ cup margarine
4 eggs
½ tsp. baking powder
1 zucchini, grated
½ cup feta cheese, crumbled
⅓ cup flour
½ cup spinach, cooked
4 tbsps. parsley, chopped
½ tsp. nutmeg
¼ cup water
¼ tsp. pepper
¼ tsp. salt
4 onion spring, chopped

Directions:
1. Preheat the air fryer to 370 degrees Fahrenheit. Whisk together eggs, water, margarine, and salt in a mixing bowl. Mix in the baking soda and flour thoroughly. Combine the onions, nutmeg, parsley, spinach, and zucchini in a large mixing bowl. Mix thoroughly.
2. Stir in the feta cheese thoroughly. Season with salt and pepper.
3. Place the silicone muffin molds in the air fryer basket and pour the batter into them.
4. Muffins should be cooked for 20 minutes.
5. Finally, serve and enjoy.

2. Breakfast Casserole

Prep time: 10 minutes / Cooking Time: 28 Minutes/ Total time: 38 minutes / Yield: 4 Servings.

Ingredients:

⅔ cup chicken broth
2 eggs
4 tsps. pine nuts, minced
1 lb. beef
4 egg whites
¼ cup red pepper, roasted and sliced
¼ cup pesto sauce
tsp. pepper
¼ tsp. sea salt

Directions:

1. Preheat the air fryer to 370 degrees Fahrenheit. Set aside the air fryer pan after spraying it with cooking spray.
2. In a separate pan, heat the oil over medium heat. Cook the beef in a pan until golden brown.
3. Drain excess oil and spread it into the prepared pan after it's done cooking.
4. In a bowl, whisk together the other ingredients (except the pine nuts) and pour over the sauce.
5. Cook for 25-28 minutes in the air fryer with the pan.
6. Serve with pine nuts on top.

Nutrition per serving: Calories: 624; Fat: 49g; Protein: 39g; Carbohydrates: 2g; Sugar: 2.1g; Cholesterol: 200mg

3. Broccoli Muffins

Prep time: 10 minutes / Cooking Time: 24 Minutes/ Total time: 34 minutes / Yield: 6 Servings.

Ingredients:
2 large eggs
Cup broccoli florets, chopped
1 cup almond milk, unsweetened
Cups almond flour
2 tbsps. nutritional yeast
½ tsp sea salt
1 tsp. baking powder

Directions:
1. Preheat the air fryer to 325 degrees Fahrenheit.
2. In a large mixing basin, combine all of the ingredients and stir until well blended.
3. Place the silicone muffin molds in the air fryer basket and pour the mixture into them.
4. Bake for 20 to 24 minutes, depending on the size of the muffins.
5. Serve your muffins and enjoy.

Nutrition per serving: Calories: 235; Fat: 21.1g; Protein: 12.1g; Carbohydrates: 11g; Sugar: 1.7g; Cholesterol: 62mg

4. Pepper Egg Bites

Prep time: 15 minutes / Cooking Time: 15 Minutes/ Total time: 30 minutes / Yield: 7 Servings.

Ingredients:
3 tbsp. scallions, minced
5 large eggs, beaten
3 tbsps. 2% milk

½ tsp. marjoram, dried

tsp. salt

Pinch freshly ground black pepper

½ cup Colby or Muenster cheese, shredded

⅓ cup bell pepper, minced, any color

Directions:

1. Whisk together the eggs, milk, marjoram, salt, and black pepper in a medium mixing bowl until well blended.

2. Add the bell peppers, scallions, and cheese and mix well. Fill the 7 egg bite cups halfway with the egg mixture, making sure each cup has part of the solids. Preheat the air fryer to 325 degrees Fahrenheit.

3. Make a sling out of foil: Fold an 18-inch length of heavy-duty aluminum foil into thirds lengthwise. Lower the egg bite pan into the air fryer using this sling.

4. Keep the foil in the air fryer, but bend the sides down to fit the equipment.

5. Bake for 10–15 minutes, or until a toothpick inserted in the center comes out clean.

6. Remove the egg bite pan using the foil sling. Allow 5 minutes to cool before inverting the pan onto a dish to remove the egg bites.

7. Serve warm and enjoy.

Nutrition per serving: *Calories: 86.8; Fat: 6g; Protein: 7g; Carbohydrates: 1g; Sodium: 149mg; Cholesterol: 141mg*

5. Zucchini Gratin

Prep time: 10 minutes / Cooking Time: 24 Minutes/ Total time: 34 minutes / Yield: 4 Servings.

Ingredients:

3 medium zucchinis, sliced

1 large egg, lightly beaten

1 tbsp. Dijon mustard

1 ¼ cup almond milk, unsweetened
½ cup nutritional yeast
1 tsp. sea salt

Directions:
1. Preheat the air fryer to 370 degrees Fahrenheit.
2. Arrange zucchini slices in the baking dish of an air fryer.
3. Heat almond milk in a saucepan over low heat, then whisk in Dijon mustard, nutritional yeast, and sea salt.
4. Whisk in the beaten egg well.
5. Cook for 20-24 minutes in the air fryer with the dish
6. Serve and enjoy.

Nutrition per serving: *Calories: 120; Fat: 3.4g; Protein: 12.6g; Carbohydrates: 14g; Sugar: 2; Cholesterol: 47mg*

6. Crunchy Nut Granola

Prep time: 10 minutes / Cooking Time: 15 Minutes/ Total time: 25 minutes / Yield: 6 Servings.

Ingredients:
Nonstick baking spray (containing flour)
¼ cup honey
2 cups old-fashioned oats, rolled
¼ cup pecans, chopped
¼ cup cashews, chopped
¼ cup pistachios
2 tbsps. light brown sugar
3 tbsps. vegetable oil
½ tsp. ground cinnamon
½ cup cherries, dried

Directions:
1. Toss the oats, pistachios, pecans, and cashews together in a medium bowl.
2. Combine the honey, brown sugar, vegetable oil, and cinnamon in a small pot. Cook, stirring often, over low heat

until the mixture is smooth, about 4 minutes. Pour the liquid over the oat mixture and whisk to combine.

3. Using baking spray, coat a 7-inch spring form pan. Toss in the granola mix.

4. Preheat the air fryer to 325 degrees Fahrenheit. In the air fryer basket, place the pan.

Cook for 7 minutes before removing the pan from the heat and stirring. Cook for another 6 to 9 minutes, or until the granola has turned a light golden-brown color. Add the dried cherries and mix well.

5. Take the pan out of the air fryer and let it aside to cool, stirring a few times while the granola cools.

6. Keep for up to 4 days in an airtight jar at room temperature.

Nutrition per serving: *Calories: 446; Sat Fat: 5g; Total Fat: 18g; Protein: 11.5g; Carbohydrates: 64g; Sodium: 52mg*

7. Avocado Flautist

Prep time: 10 minutes / Cooking Time: 25 Minutes/ Total time: 35 minutes / Yield: 7-8 Servings.

Ingredients:
1 tbsp. olive oil
8 eggs, beaten
½ tsp. salt
¼ tsp. pepper
8 tortillas, fajita-size
1 ½ tsp. cumin
1 tsp. chili powder
8 slices bacon, cooked
4 oz. cream cheese, softened

Avocado Crème:
2 small avocados
1 lime, juiced
½ cup Greek yogurt

½ tsp. salt
¼ tsp. pepper

Directions:
1. Heat the olive oil in a skillet and add the eggs, salt, cumin, pepper, and chili powder, stirring constantly for 4 minutes. Spread cream cheese on all of the tortillas and top with bacon. The egg scramble is then divided on top, followed by the cheese.
2. Roll the tortillas in order to seal in the contents. In the Air Fryer basket, place four rolls. Close the lid on the Air Fryer toaster oven and place the Air Fryer basket inside. Select the Air Fry mode and set the temperature to 400 degrees F for 12 minutes.
3. Repeat the process with the remaining tortilla rolls. Meanwhile, combine the ingredients for the avocado crème in a blender.
4. Serve with hot flautas.

Nutrition per serving: *Calories: 212; Fat: 11.6g; Protein: 17.3g; Carbs: 14.6g*

8. Veggie Frittata

Prep time: 15 minutes / Cooking Time: 25 Minutes/ Total time: 40 minutes / Yield: 4 Servings.

Ingredients:
1 cup Cheddar cheese, shredded and divided
¼ cup yellow summer squash, chopped
2 tbsps. scallion, chopped
¼ cup red bell pepper, chopped
5 large eggs, beaten
¼ tsp. sea salt
Tsp. freshly ground black pepper

Directions:

1. Combine the bell pepper, summer squash, and scallion in a 7-inch cake pan.

2. Preheat the air fryer to 350 degrees Fahrenheit. In the air fryer basket, place the cake pan. Cook for 3 to 4 minutes, or until the vegetables are crisp-tender. Remove the pan from the air fryer and set it aside.

3. In a medium mixing bowl, whisk together the eggs, salt, and pepper. Add half of the Cheddar and mix well. Pour the contents of the pan into the vegetables.

4. Return the pan to the air fryer and cook for another 10 to 15 minutes, then sprinkle the remaining cheese over the frittata. Cook for 4 to 5 minutes more, or until the cheese has melted and the frittata has set.

5. To serve, cut into wedges.

Nutrition per serving: *Calories: 260; Sat Fat: 10.6g; Total Fat: 21g; Protein: 15g; Carbohydrates: 2g; Sodium: 463mg; Cholesterol: 277mg*

9. Morning Potatoes

Prep time: 10 minutes / Cooking Time: 23 Minutes/ Total time: 33 minutes / Yield: 4-5 Servings.

Ingredients:

Parsley, chopped, for garnish
2 russet potatoes, washed and diced
1 tbsp. olive oil
½ tsp. salt
¼ tsp. garlic powder

Directions:

1. Soak the potatoes for 45 minutes in cold water, then drain and dry.

2. In the Air Fryer basket, toss potato cubes with garlic powder, salt, and olive oil.

3. Close the lid of the Air Fryer toaster oven and place the Air Fryer basket inside.
Select the Air Fry setting and cook for 23 minutes at 400°F.
4. When they're halfway done, toss them well and continue cooking.
5. Garnish with chopped parsley and serve

Nutrition per serving: *Calories: 146; Fat: 5g; Protein: 6g; Carbs: 42g*

10. Ham, Mushroom & Tomato Frittata

Prep time: 15 minutes / Cooking Time: 16 Minutes/ Total time: 31 minutes / Yield: 2 Servings.

Ingredients:
6 cherry tomatoes, halved
1 ham slice, cooked and chopped
Salt and ground black pepper, as required
6 fresh mushrooms, sliced
3 eggs
1 tbsp. fresh parsley, chopped

Directions:
1. Combine the ham, tomatoes, mushrooms, salt, and black pepper in a baking pan and combine thoroughly.
2. Select the "Air Fry" mode by pressing the "Power Button" on the Air Fry Oven and turning the dial.
3. To adjust the cooking duration to 16 minutes, press the Time button and then turn the dial again.
4. Now press the Temp button and rotate the dial to 320 degrees Fahrenheit.
5. To begin, press the "Start/Pause" button.
6. Open the lid when the machine beeps to indicate that it has preheated.
7. Place the pan on top of the "Wire Rack" and place it in the oven.

8. In a separate dish, beat the eggs thoroughly.
9. Stir in the parsley thoroughly.
10. After 6 minutes of cooking, evenly spread the egg mixture over the ham mixture.
11. Cut into wedges of similar size and serve.

Nutrition per serving: *Calories: 227; Sat Fat: 5.3g; Total Fat: 15.4g; Total Carbs: 3.5g; Fiber: 0.9 g; Sodium: 608mg; Cholesterol: 277mg; Sugar: 2.1g*

11. Potato Jalapeno Hash

Prep time: 15 minutes / Cooking Time: 24 Minutes/ Total time: 39 minutes / Yield: 4 Servings.

Ingredients:
1 tbsp. olive oil
1 red bell pepper, seeded and diced
1 ½ lbs. potatoes, peeled and diced
Salt and black pepper to taste
1 small onion, chopped
1 jalapeno, seeded and diced
½ tsp. olive oil
½ tsp. taco seasoning mix
½ tsp. ground cumin

Directions:
1. Soak the potatoes for 20 minutes in cold water before draining them.
2. Toss the potatoes with 1 tablespoon of extra virgin olive oil. In the Air Fryer basket, spread them out. Close the lid on the Air Fryer toaster oven and place the Air Fryer basket inside. Select the Air Fry setting and cook for 18 minutes at 370°F.
3. In a salad bowl, combine the onion, pepper, olive oil, taco spice, and all other ingredients.

4. Return the Air Fryer basket to the oven with this vegetable mixture. Cook for another 6 minutes at 356°F.
5. Serve immediately while warm.

Nutrition per serving: *Calories: 242; Fat: 14.5g; Protein: 8.9g; Carbs: 36.6g*

12. Turkey, Spinach & Broccoli Frittata

Prep time: 15 minutes / Cooking Time: 30 Minutes/ Total time: 45 minutes / Yield: 4 Servings.

Ingredients:
6 eggs
tsp. hot sauce
1 tsp. olive oil
6 turkey sausage links, cut into small pieces
1 cup broccoli florets, cut into small pieces
½ cup fresh spinach, chopped up
2 tbsps. half-and-half
tsp. garlic salt
Salt and ground black pepper, as required

Directions:
1. Heat the olive oil in a skillet over medium heat and brown the sausage for about 7-8 minutes.
2. Cook for 3-4 minutes after adding the broccoli.
3. Cook for about 2-3 minutes after adding the spinach.
4. Remove the pan from the heat and leave it aside to cool for a few minutes.
5. Meanwhile, in a mixing bowl, whisk together the eggs, half-and-half, spicy sauce, garlic salt, salt, and black pepper.
6. Place the broccoli mixture in the bottom of a lightly greased pan and top with the egg mixture.
7. Select the "Air Bake" mode by pressing the "Power Button" on the Air Fry Oven and turning the dial.

8. To set the cooking time to 15 minutes, press the Time button and then turn the dial again.

9. Now press the Temp button and rotate the dial to 400 degrees Fahrenheit.

10. To begin, press the "Start/Pause" button.

11. Open the lid when the appliance beeps to indicate that it is preheated.

12. Place the pan in the oven on top of the "Wire Rack."

13. Once done, cut it into equal-sized slices and serve warm.

Nutrition per serving: Calories: 339; Sat Fat: 11.6g; Total Fat: 27.5g; Total Carbs: 3.6g; Fiber: 0.7g; Sodium: 596mg; Cholesterol: 229mg; Sugar: 1.6g.

13. Trout Frittata

Prep time: 15 minutes / Cooking Time: 25 Minutes/ Total time: 40 minutes / Yield: 4 Servings.

Ingredients:
6 eggs
1 tbsp. olive oil
1 onion, sliced
¼ cup fresh dill, chopped
½ tbsp. horseradish sauce
2 tbsps. crème fraiche
2 trout fillets, hot-smoked and chopped

Directions:
1. Heat the oil in a skillet over medium heat and sauté the onion for 4 to 5 minutes.

2. Take the pan from the heat and set it aside.

3. In a separate bowl, whisk together the eggs, horseradish sauce, and crème fraiche.

4. Arrange the sautéed onion in the bottom of a baking pan, then top with the egg mixture, then the fish.

5. Select the "Air Fry" mode by pressing the "Power Button" on the Air Fry Oven and turning the dial.

6. To adjust the cooking duration to 20 minutes, press the Time button and then turn the dial again.

7. Now press the Temp button and rotate the dial to 320 degrees Fahrenheit.

8. To begin, press the "Start/Pause" button.

9. Open the lid when the unit beeps to indicate that it is preheated.

10. Place the pan on top of the "Wire Rack" and place it in the oven.

11. When ready, cut into equal-sized wedges and garnish with dill before serving.

Nutrition per serving: *Calories: 258; Sat Fat: 3.8g; Total Fat: 15.7g; Total Carbs: 5.1g; Fiber: 1g; Sodium: 141mg; Cholesterol: 288mg; Sugar: 1.7g*

14. Spicy Sweet Potato Hash

Prep time: 10 minutes / Cooking Time: 16 Minutes/ Total time: 26 minutes / Yield: 4 Servings.

Ingredients:
2 slices ham, cooked and diced
2 tbsp. olive oil
2 large sweet potato, diced
paprika, smoked
1 tsp. sea salt
1 tsp. dill weed, dried
1 tsp. ground black pepper

Directions:
1. In the Air Fry basket, toss sweet potato with all of the spices and olive oil.

2. Close the cover of the Air Fryer toaster oven and place the Air Fryer basket inside.

3. Preheat the oven to 400°F and cook for 16 minutes in the Air Fry mode.
4. After every 5 minutes, toss the potatoes.
5. Toss in the ham and serve warm.

Nutrition per serving: *Calories: 134; Fat: 5.9g; Protein: 6.6g; Carbs: 36.6g*

15. Delicious Potato Hash

Prep time: 10 minutes / Cooking Time: 25 Minutes/ Total time: 35 minutes / Yield: 4 Servings.

Ingredients:
1-½ potatoes, cubed
1 yellow onion, chopped
2 tsps. olive oil
1 green bell pepper, chopped
Salt and black pepper to the taste
½ tsp. thyme, dried
2 eggs

Directions:
1. Preheat your air fryer at 350 degrees Fahrenheit, add the oil, heat it up, then add the onion, bell pepper, salt, and pepper, stir, and cook for 5 minutes.
2. Combine the potatoes, thyme, and eggs in a mixing bowl. Stir well, cover, and bake for 20 minutes at 360°F.
3. Serve for breakfast by dividing the mixture among dishes.

Nutrition per serving: *Calories: 241; Fat: 4g; Protein: 7g; Carbs: 12g; Fiber; 7g.*

CHAPTER 4: Lunch Recipes

1. Flavorful Steak

Prep time: 10 minutes / Cooking Time: 18 Minutes/ Total time: 28 minutes / Yield: 2 Servings.

Ingredients:
½ tsp. garlic powder
2 steaks, rinsed and pat dry
1 tsp. olive oil
Salt
Pepper

Directions:
1. Drizzle olive oil over the steaks and season with garlic powder, pepper, and salt.
2. Preheat the oven of the instant vortex air fryer to 400 degrees Fahrenheit.
3. Place the steaks on an air fryer oven pan and cook for 10 to 18 minutes, flipping halfway through.
4. Serve and enjoy.

Nutrition per serving: *Calories: 361; Fat: 10.9g; Protein: 61.6g; Carbs: 0.5g*

2. Juicy Pork Chops

Prep time: 10 minutes / Cooking Time: 16 Minutes/ Total time: 26 minutes / Yield: 3-4 Servings.

Ingredients:
4 pork chops, boneless
½ tsp. celery seed
2 tsp. olive oil
½ tsp. salt
parsley
½ tsp. garlic, granulated
½ tsp. onion, granulated

¼ tsp. sugar

Directions:
1. Combine oil, celery seed, parsley, granulated onion, granulated garlic, sugar, and salt in a small bowl.
2. Rub the pork chops all over with the spice mixture.
3. Place the pork chops on the air fryer oven pan and bake for 8 minutes at 350°F.
4. Toss the pork chops over and cook for another 8 minutes.
5. Finally, serve and enjoy.

Nutrition per serving: *Calories: 279; Fat: 22g; Protein: 18g; Carbs: 0.6g*

3. Crispy Meatballs

Prep time: 10 minutes / Cooking Time: 13 Minutes/ Total time: 30 minutes / Yield: 8 Servings.

Ingredients:
2 eggs, lightly beaten
1 lb. pork, ground
1 lb. beef, ground
½ cup breadcrumbs
1 tbsp. Worcestershire sauce
½ cup feta cheese, crumbled
¼ cup fresh parsley, chopped
1 tbsp. garlic, minced
1 tsp. salt
1 onion, chopped
¼ tsp. pepper

Directions:
1. In a mixing basin, add all of the ingredients and stir until well blended.
2. Spray a tray pan in the air fryer oven with cooking spray.
3. Form tiny balls from the meat mixture and place on a pan to air fry for 10-13 minutes at 400oF.

4. Serve and enjoy.

Nutrition per serving: Calories: 263; Fat: 9g; Protein: 36g; Carbs: 7.5g

4. Lemon Garlic Lamb Chops

Prep time: 10 minutes / Cooking Time: 6 Minutes/ Total time: 16 minutes / Yield: 6 Servings.

Ingredients:
1 ½ tbsp. lemon zest
6 lamb loin chops
2 tbsps. fresh lemon juice
1 tbsp. olive oil
1 tbsp. garlic, minced
1 tbsp. rosemary, dried
Pepper
Salt

Directions:
1. In a mixing dish, place the lamb chops. Add the other ingredients to the lamb chops and toss well to coat.
2. Place lamb chops on an air fryer oven tray and air fry for 3 minutes at 400°F. Turn the lamb chops over and air fry for another 3 minutes.
3. Serve and enjoy.

Nutrition per serving: Calories: 69; Fat: 6g; Protein: 3g; Carbs: 1.2g

5. Easy Rosemary Lamb Chops

Prep time: 10 minutes / Cooking Time: 6 Minutes/ Total time: 16 minutes / Yield: 4 Servings.

Ingredients:
4 lamb chops
2 tbsps. rosemary, dried
¼ cup fresh lemon juice

Pepper
Salt

Directions:

1. Combine the lemon juice, rosemary, pepper, and salt in a small bowl.
Brush the lamb chops with a combination of lemon juice and rosemary.
2. Place lamb chops on an air fryer oven tray and cook for 3 minutes at 400°F. 3. Cook for another 3 minutes on the other side of the lamb chops.
4. Serve and enjoy.

Nutrition per serving: *Calories: 267; Fat: 21.7g; Protein: 61.9g; Carbs: 1.4g*

6. BBQ Pork Ribs

Prep time: 10 minutes / Cooking Time: 12 Minutes/ Total time: 22 minutes / Yield: 6 Servings.

Ingredients:
½ cup BBQ sauce
1 slab baby back pork ribs, cut into pieces
Salt
½ tsp. paprika

Directions:

1. In a mixing bowl, combine the pork ribs. Set aside for 30 minutes after coating pork ribs with BBQ sauce, paprika, and salt.
2. Preheat the oven of the instant vortex air fryer to 350 degrees Fahrenheit. Cook for 10-12 minutes on an instant vortex air fryer oven pan with marinated pork ribs. Halfway through, turn around.
3. Serve and enjoy.

Nutrition per serving: Calories: 145; Fat: 7g; Protein: 9.1g; Carbs: 9.9g

7. Classic Beef Jerky

Prep time: 10 minutes / Cooking Time: 4 Hours/ Total time: 30 minutes / Yield: 4 Servings.

Ingredients:
¾ tsp. garlic powder
1 tsp. onion powder
3 tbsps. brown sugar
3 tbsps. soy sauce
2 lbs. London broil, sliced thinly
1 tsp. olive oil

Directions:
1. In a large zip-lock bag, combine all ingredients except the meat.
2. Stir until everything is fully blended. Fill the bag with meat.
3. Close the bag and gently massage the meat to coat it in the marinade.
4. Allow the meat to marinade for 1 hour.
5. Place marinated pork slices on an instant vortex air fryer tray and dehydrate for 4 hours at 160°F.
6. Serve and enjoy.

Nutrition per serving: Calories: 133 Fat: 4.7g; Protein: 13.5g; Carbs: 9.4g.

8. Bacon Wrapped Filet Mignon

Prep time: 10 minutes / Cooking Time: 15 Minutes/ Total time: 25 minutes / Yield: 7 Servings.

Ingredients:
2 (4-oz.) filet mignon
2 bacon slices
Salt and ground black pepper, as required

Olive oil cooking spray

Directions:

1. Secure each filet mignon with toothpicks after wrapping 1 bacon slice around it.
2. Lightly season the filets with salt and black pepper.
3. Spray the filet mignon with cooking spray and place it on a grilling rack.
4. Place the drip pan in the cooking chamber of the Instant Vortex plus Air Fryer Oven.
5. Select "Air Fry" and set the temperature to 375 degrees Fahrenheit.
6. Press the "Start" button and set the timer for 15 minutes.
7. Place the frying rack in the center position when the display says "Add Food."
8. Turn the filets when the display says "Turn Food."
9. Remove the rack from the Vortex when the cooking time is up and serve hot.

Nutrition per serving: Calories: 360; Fat: 19.6g; Protein: 42.6g; Carbs: 0.4g

9. Honey Mustard Pork Tenderloin

Prep time: 10 minutes / Cooking Time: 26 Minutes/ Total time: 36 minutes / Yield: 4 Servings.

Ingredients:
1 lb. pork tenderloin
1 tbsp. garlic, minced
1 tsp. sriracha sauce
2 tbsps. soy sauce
¾ tbsp. Dijon mustard
1 ½ tbsp. honey
1 tbsp. mustard

Directions:
1. In a large zip-lock bag, combine the sriracha sauce, garlic, soy sauce, honey, Dijon mustard, and mustard.
2. Fill the bag with pork tenderloin. Place the bag in the refrigerator for the night. Preheat the oven of the quick vortex air fryer to 380°F.
3. Spray a tray in the instant vortex air fryer with cooking spray, then set the marinated pork tenderloin on it and air fry for 26 minutes.
4. After every 5 minutes, turn the pork tenderloin.
5. Cut into slices and serve.

Nutrition per serving: Calories: 195; Fat: 4.1g; Protein: 30.5g; Carbs: 8.1g

10. Beef Burgers

Prep time: 15 minutes / Cooking Time: 18 Minutes/ Total time: 33 minutes / Yield: 4 Servings.

Ingredients:
For Burgers:
½ cup panko breadcrumbs
1-lb. beef, ground
¼ cup onion, chopped finely
3 tsps. low-sodium soy sauce
3 tbsps. Dijon mustard
2 tsps. fresh rosemary, finely chopped
Salt, to taste
For Topping:
1 tbsp. brown sugar
4 Gruyere cheese slices
2 tbsps. Dijon mustard
1 tsp. soy sauce

Directions:
1. Combine all of the ingredients in a large mixing basin and stir until well blended.
2. Form the ingredients into four equal-sized patties.
3. Place the patties on a baking sheet.
4. Place the drip pan in the cooking chamber of the Instant Vortex Plus Air Fryer Oven.
5. Select "Air Fry" and set the temperature to 370 degrees Fahrenheit.
6. Press the "Start" button and set the timer for 15 minutes.
7. Place the frying rack in the center position when the display says "Add Food."
8. Turn the burgers when the display says "Turn Food."
9. Meanwhile, make the sauce by mixing together the mustard, brown sugar, and soy sauce in a small bowl.
10. Remove the tray from the Vortex when the cooking time is up and coat the burgers with the sauce.
11. Place 1 slice of cheese on top of each burger.
12. Place the tray in the cooking chamber and turn on the broiler.
13. Press the "Start" button and set the timer for 3 minutes.
14. Remove the tray from the Vortex when the cooking time is finished and serve hot.

Nutrition per serving: *Calories: 402; Fat: 17.7g; Protein: 44.6g; Carbs: 6.4g*

11. Sweet & Spicy Meatballs

Prep time: 20 minutes / Cooking Time: 30 Minutes/ Total time: 50 minutes / Yield: 8 Servings.

Ingredients:
For Meatballs:
⅔ cup quick-cooking oats
½ cup Ritz crackers, crushed
2 lbs. lean ground beef

1 (5-oz.) can milk, evaporated
2 large eggs, lightly beaten
1 tsp. honey
1 tsp. ground cumin
1 tbsp. onion, dried and minced
1 tsp. garlic powder
Salt and ground black pepper, as required

For Sauce:
⅓ cup honey
⅓ cup orange marmalade
⅓ cup brown sugar
1 tbsp. Worcestershire sauce
2 tbsps. soy sauce
1-2 tbsps. hot sauce
2 tbsps. cornstarch

Directions:
1. **To make meatballs:** combine all of the ingredients in a large mixing basin and mix well.
2. Roll the mixture into 112-inch balls.
3. Arrange half of the meatballs in a single layer on a baking sheet.
4. Place the drip pan in the cooking chamber of the Instant Vortex Plus Air Fryer Oven.
5. Select "Air Fry" and set the temperature to 380 degrees Fahrenheit.
6. Press the "Start" button and set the timer for 15 minutes.
7. Place the cooking tray in the center position when the display says "Add Food."
8. Turn the meatballs when the display says "Turn Food."
9. Remove the tray from the Vortex when the cooking time is finished.
10. Repeat with the rest of the meatballs.

11. **Meanwhile, for sauce:** in a small saucepan, combine all of the ingredients and simmer over medium heat, stirring constantly, until thickened.

12. Toss the meatballs in the sauce and serve.

Nutrition per serving: *Calories: 411; Fat: 11g; Protein: 38.7g; Carbs: 38.9g*

12. Greek Lamb Chops

Prep time: 10 minutes / Cooking Time: 10 Minutes/ Total time: 20 minutes / Yield: 4 Servings.

Ingredients:
2 tsps. garlic, minced
2 lbs. lamb chops
1 ½ tsp. oregano, dried
¼ cup olive oil
¼ cup fresh lemon juice
½ tsp. pepper
1 tsp. salt

Directions:
1. In a mixing dish, place the lamb chops. Coat the lamb chops well with the remaining ingredients.
2. Place the lamb chops on the air fryer oven pan and cook for 5 minutes at 400oF.
3. Flip the lamb chops and cook for another 5 minutes.
4. Finally, serve and enjoy.

Nutrition per serving: *Calories: 537; Fat: 29.4g; Protein: 64.1g; Carbs: 1.3g*

13. Our Daily Bean

Prep time: 5 minutes / Cooking Time: 8 Minutes/ Total time: 13 minutes / Yield: 2 Servings.

Ingredients:
Cooking oil spray (sunflower, safflower)

¼ cup tomato sauce
1 (15-oz.) can pinto beans, drained
2 tbsps. Nutrition yeast
2 large garlic cloves, pressed or minced
½ tsp. dried oregano
tsp. freshly ground black pepper ½ tsp. cumin
¼ tsp. sea salt

Directions:
1. Combine the beans, tomato sauce, nutrition yeast, garlic, oregano, cumin, salt, and pepper in a medium mixing bowl.
2. Lightly grease a 6-inch round, 2-inch deep baking pan and pour the bean mixture into it. 4 minutes in the oven
3. Remove the pan from the oven, stir well, and bake for another 4 minutes, or until the mixture has thickened and is thoroughly cooked. It will probably build a crust on top and become lightly browned in sections.
4. Serve warm. This can be stored for up to a week in an airtight container.

Nutrition per serving: *Calories: 284; Sat Fat: 1g; Total Fat: 4g; Protein: 20g; Carbohydrates: 47g; Sodium: 807mg; Cholesterol: 0mg; Fiber: 16g*

14. Crispy Baked Avocado Tacos

Prep time: 10 minutes / Cooking Time: 20 Minutes/ Total time: 30 minutes / Yield: 5 Servings.

Ingredients:
Salsa:
1 clove garlic, minced
1 Roma tomato, finely chopped
1 cup pineapple, finely shopped
½ red bell pepper, finely chopped
½ jalapeno, finely chopped
½ of a medium red onion
Pinch each cumin and salt

Avocado tacos:
¼ cup all-purpose flour 35g
½ cup panko crumbs 65g
1 avocado
1 large egg whisked
4 flour tortillas click for recipes
Pinch each salt and pepper

Adobo Sauce:
¼ tsp. lime juice
¼ cup plain yogurt (60g)
2 tbsps. Mayonnaise (30g)
1 tbsp. Adobo sauce from a jar of chipotle peppers Polte peppers

Directions:
1. Salsa: Combine all the salsa ingredients and put them in the fridge.
2. To prepare the avocado, cut it in half lengthwise and remove the pit.
Cut each half of an avocado into four equal pieces with the skin facing down. Then
Peel the skin away from the body gently.
3. Preheat the oven to 230°C (440°F) or the air fryer to 200°C (400°F).
190 degrees Celsius (374 degrees Fahrenheit). Arrange your work space so that you have a bowl of flour, a measuring cup, and a knife.
At the end, a baking sheet coated with paper, a whisk, and a bowl of Panko with S&P.
4. Coat: Toss each avocado slice in flour, then in egg, and then in flour again.
the panko breadcrumbs Bake for 10 minutes on the prepared baking sheet or fry in the air. After the very first half of the cooking time, lightly brown

5. Sauce: Combine all of the sauce ingredients while the avocados are frying.

6. To serve, top a tortilla with salsa, 2 slices of avocado, and a drizzle of sauce. Serve right away and enjoy!

Nutrition per serving: Calories: 193; Fat: 13.7g; Protein: 13.7g; Carbohydrates: 4.69g

15. Easy Beef Roast

Prep time: 10 minutes / Cooking Time: 45 Minutes/ Total time: 55 minutes / Yield: 6 Servings.

Ingredients:

2 ½ lbs. beef roast

2 tbsps. Italian seasoning

Directions:

1. Place the roast on the rotisserie.

2. Season the roast with Italian seasoning before placing it in the instant vortex air fryer.

3. Air fry for 45 minutes at 350°F or until the internal temperature of the beef roast reaches 145°F (as measured by a meat thermometer).

4. Cut into slices and serve.

Nutrition per serving: *Calories: 365; Fat: 13.2g; Protein: 57.5g; Carbs: 0.5g*

CHAPTER 5: Sides and Snacks

1. Kale and Celery Crackers

Prep Time: 30 Minutes / Cooking Time: 20 Minutes/ Total Time: 40 Minutes / Yield: 6 Servings.

Ingredients:
1 bunch basil; chopped
1/3 cup olive oil2 cups flax seed; ground2 cups flax seed; soaked overnight and drained 4 bunches kale; chopped
4 garlic cloves; minced
1/2 bunch celery; chopped.

Direction:
1. Blend ground flaxseed with celery, kale, basil, and garlic in a food processor until smooth.
2. Blend in the oil and soaked flaxseed, then distribute in the air fryer pan, cutting into medium crackers and cooking for 20 minutes at 380°F.
3. Serve as an appetizer by dividing into bowls.

Nutrition per serving: Calories: 143; Fat: 1g; Protein: 4g; Carbs: 8g; Fiber: 2g.

2. Delicious Tuna Cakes

Prep Time: 20 Minutes / Cooking Time: 10 Minutes/ Total Time: 30 Minutes / Yield: 12 Servings.

Ingredients:
Cooking spray
1 tsp. parsley; dried
1/2 cup red onion; chopped.
1 tsp. garlic powder
15 oz. canned tuna; drain and flaked
3 eggs
1/2 tsp. dill; dried
Salt and black pepper to the taste

Direction:
1. Combine tuna, salt, pepper, dill, parsley, onion, garlic powder, and eggs in a mixing bowl; whisk well and form medium cakes from the mixture.
2. Place tuna cakes in the air fryer basket, drizzle with cooking oil, and cook for 10 minutes at 350°F, flipping halfway through.
3. Serve as an appetizer by arranging them on a platter.

Nutrition per serving: *Calories: 140; Fat: 2g; Protein: 5.8g; Carbs: 1g; Fiber: 1g.*

3. Party Pork Rolls

Prep Time: 50 Minutes / Cooking Time: 35 Minutes/ Total Time: 1 Hour & 25 Minutes / Yield: 4 Servings.

Ingredients:
3 tbsp. parsley; chopped
1/2 tsp. chili powder
1 (15 oz.) pork fillet
1 tsp. cinnamon powder
1 red onion; chopped
1 garlic clove; minced
2 tbsp. olive oil
1 ½ tsp. cumin; ground
Salt and black pepper to the taste

Direction:
1. Combine cinnamon, garlic, salt, pepper, chili powder, oil, onion, parsley, and cumin in a mixing bowl and mix well.
2. Place the pork fillet on a cutting board and use a meat tenderizer to flatten it. Also, flatten it with a meat tenderizer.
3. Spread onion mixture on pork, roll tightly, cut into medium rolls, and cook for 35 minutes in a preheated air fryer at 360°F.
4. Serve as an appetizer by arranging them on a dish.

Nutrition per serving: Calories: 340; Fat: 12g; Protein: 23g; Carbs: 15g; Fiber: 1g.

4. Mouthwatering Beef Rolls

Prep Time: 24 Minutes / Cooking Time: 14 Minutes/ Total Time: 38 Minutes / Yield: 4 Servings.

Ingredients:
2 lbs. beef steak; opened and flattened with a meat tenderizer
3 oz. red bell
pepper; roasted and chopped.
Salt and black pepper to the taste
6 slices provolone cheese
1 cup baby spinach
3 tbsp. pesto

Direction:
1. Place a flattened beef steak on a chopping board, spread pesto all over, layer cheese in a single layer, add bell peppers, spinach, and season to taste with salt and pepper.
2. Roll your steak, secure using toothpicks, and season again with salt and pepper; place roll in air fryer basket and cook for 14 minutes at 400°F, turning halfway through. Allow it cool before cutting into 2-inch smaller rolls.
3. Serve as an appetizer by arranging them on a platter.

Nutrition per serving: Calories: 230; Fat: 1g; Protein: 10g; Carbs: 12g; Fiber: 2.9g.

5. Easy Broccoli Patties

Prep Time: 20 Minutes / Cooking Time: 10 Minutes/ Total Time: 30 Minutes / Yield: 7 Servings.

Ingredients:
2 cups cheddar cheese; grated
4 cups broccoli florets
1/2 tsp. baking soda
1 ½ cup almond flour

1 tsp. paprika

2 eggs

1/4 cup olive oil

1 tsp. garlic powder

1/2 tsp. apple cider vinegar

Salt and black pepper to the taste

Direction:

1. Place broccoli florets in a food processor with salt and pepper; process until smooth, then transfer to a bowl.

2. Combine almond flour, salt, pepper, paprika, garlic powder, baking soda, cheese, oil, eggs, and vinegar in a mixing bowl and whisk well. Form 12 patties from the mixture.

3. Place them in the basket of your preheated air fryer and cook for 10 minutes at 350°F.

4. Serve patties as an appetizer by arranging them on a platter.

Nutrition per serving: Calories: 203; Fat: 12g; Protein: 2g; Carbs: 14.2g; Fiber: 2g.

6. Amazing Seafood Appetizer

Prep Time: 35 Minutes / Cooking Time: 25 Minutes/ Total Time: 1 Hour / Yield: 4 Servings.

Ingredients:

1 cup homemade mayonnaise

1/2 cup yellow onion; chopped.

1 cup green bell pepper; chopped.

1 cup crabmeat; flaked

1 cup celery; chopped.

1 cup baby shrimp; peeled and deveined

2 tbsp. bread crumbs

Salt and black pepper to the taste

1 tsp. Worcestershire sauce

1 tbsp. butter

1 tsp. sweet paprika

Direction:
1. In a mixing bowl, combine shrimp, crab meat, bell pepper, onion, mayonnaise, celery, salt, and pepper.
2. Stir in the Worcestershire sauce, then pour everything into an air fryer-safe baking dish.
3. Sprinkle bread crumbs and butter in your air fryer, then cook for 25 minutes at 320°F, shaking halfway through.
4. To serve as an appetizer, divide the mixture into a bowl and top with paprika.

Nutrition per serving: *Calories: 200; Fat: 1g; Protein: 1g; Carbs: 5g; Fiber: 2.1g.*

7. Special Empanadas

Prep Time: 35 Minutes / Cooking Time: 10 Minutes/ Total Time: 45 Minutes / Yield: 4 Servings.

Ingredients:
1 tbsp. olive oil
1 package empanada shells
1/2 tsp. cumin; ground
1/4 cup tomato salsa
1 lb. beef meat; ground
1 egg yolk whisked with 1 tbsp. water
1 yellow onion; chopped
1 green bell pepper; chopped
Salt and black pepper to the taste
2 garlic cloves; minced

Direction:
1. Heat the oil in a pan over medium-high heat, then add the beef and brown on all sides.
2. Stir in the onion, garlic, salt, pepper, bell pepper, and tomato salsa; simmer for 15 minutes, stirring occasionally.
3. Fill empanada shells halfway with cooked meat, brush with egg wash, and seal.

4. Place them in the steamer basket of your air fryer and cook for 10 minutes at 350°F.
5. Serve as an appetizer by arranging on a dish.

Nutrition per serving: *Calories: 274; Fat: 17g; Protein: 7g; Carbs: 20g; Fiber: 14g.*

8. Mexican Style Apple Snack

Prep Time: 15 Minutes / Cooking Time: 5 Minutes/ Total Time: 20 Minutes / Yield: 4 Servings.

Ingredients:
2 tsp. lemon juice
3 big apples; cored, peeled and cubed
1/2 cup clean caramel sauce
1/2 cup dark chocolate chips
1/4 cup pecans; chopped.

Direction:
1. In a mixing bowl, combine apples and lemon juice; toss well and transfer to an air fryer pan.
2. Toss in chocolate chips, pecans, and drizzled caramel sauce; place in air fryer and cook for 5 minutes at 320°F.
3. Gently toss, divide into small bowls, and serve as a snack immediately.

Nutrition per serving: *Calories: 200; Fat: 4g; Protein: 3g; Carbs: 20g; Fiber: 3g.*

9. Bacon Jalapeno Balls

Prep Time: 14 Minutes / Cooking Time: 4 Minutes/ Total Time: 18 Minutes / Yield: 3 Servings.

Ingredients:
3 oz. cream cheese
3 bacon slices; cooked and crumbled
1/4 tsp. onion powder
1/4 tsp. garlic powder

Salt and black pepper to the taste
1 jalapeno pepper; chopped.
1/2 tsp. parsley; dried

Direction:

1. In a large mixing bowl, combine cream cheese, jalapeño pepper, onion and garlic powder, parsley, bacon salt, and pepper.
2. Form tiny balls out of the mixture, set them in the air fryer basket, and cook for 4 minutes at 350°F.
4. Serve as an appetizer by arranging on a dish.

Nutrition per serving: *Calories: 172; Fat: 4g; Protein: 5g; Carbs: 12g; Fiber: 1g.*

10. Party Beef Rolls

Prep Time: 25 Minutes / Cooking Time: 15 Minutes/ Total Time: 40 Minutes / Yield: 4 Servings.

Ingredients:
4 ham slices
14 oz. beef stock
1 tbsp. butter; melted
7 oz. white wine
4 beef cutlets
8 sage leaves
Salt and black pepper to the taste

Direction:

1. Heat the stock in a skillet over medium high heat, then add the wine and cook until it reduces. Remove from heat and divide into small bowls.
2. Season the cutlets with salt and pepper, then top them with sage and ham pieces.
3. Brush the rolls with butter, lay them in the air fryer basket, and cook for 15 minutes at 400°F.
4. Arrange the rolls on a dish and serve with a side of gravy.

Nutrition per serving: *Calories: 260; Fat: 12g; Protein: 21g; Carbs: 22g; Fiber: 1g.*

11. Yummy Olives Balls

Prep Time: 14 Minutes / Cooking Time: 4 Minutes/ Total Time: 18 Minutes / Yield: 6 Servings.

Ingredients:
8 black olives; pitted and minced
14 pepperoni slices; chopped.
2 tbsp. sun dried tomato pesto
4 oz. cream cheese
Salt and black pepper to the taste
1 tbsp. basil; chopped.

Direction:
1. In a mixing bowl, combine cream cheese, salt, pepper, basil, pepperoni, pesto, and black olives; stir well and roll into small balls.
2. Place them in the basket of your air fryer and cook for 4 minutes at 350°F.
3. Serve as a snack by arranging on a tray.

Nutrition per serving: *Calories: 100; Fat: 1g; Protein: 3g; Carbs: 8g; Fiber: 0g.*

12. Cheesy Tasty Zucchini Snack

Prep Time: 18 Minutes / Cooking Time: 8 Minutes/ Total Time: 26 Minutes / Yield: 4 Servings.

Ingredients:
Cooking spray
1/4 cup tomato sauce
1 cup mozzarella; shredded
1 zucchini; sliced
Salt and black pepper to the taste
A pinch of cumin.

Direction:

1. Arrange zucchini slices in the basket of your air fryer; spray with cooking oil, spread tomato sauce all over, season with salt, pepper, and cumin, and top with mozzarella. Cook for 8 minutes at 320°F.

2. Serve as a snack by arranging them on a platter.

Nutrition per serving: Calories: 150; Fat: 1g; Protein: 4g; Carbs: 12g; Fiber: 2g.

13. Sausage Balls Snack

Preparation Time: 25 Minutes
Servings: 9

Ingredients:

4 oz. sausage meat; ground
1 tsp. sage
1/2 tsp. garlic; minced
1 small onion; chopped.
3 tbsp. breadcrumbs
Salt and black pepper to the taste

Direction:

1. In a mixing bowl, combine sausage, salt, pepper, sage, garlic, onion, and breadcrumbs; toss well and roll into small balls.

2. Place them in the basket of your air fryer and cook for 15 minutes at 360°F.

3. Serve as a snack by dividing into bowls.

Nutrition per serving: Calories: 130; Fat: 7g; Protein: 4g; Carbs: 13g; Fiber: 1g.

14. Appetizing Cajun Shrimp

Prep Time: 15 Minutes / Cooking Time: 5 Minutes/ Total Time: 20 Minutes / Yield: 2 Servings.

Ingredients:
1/4 tsp. smoked paprika
1/2 tsp. old bay seasoning
20 tiger shrimp; peeled and deveined
1 tbsp. olive oil
Salt and black pepper to the taste.

Direction:
1. Toss the shrimp in a bowl with the oil, salt, pepper, old bay spice, and paprika to coat.
2. Place shrimp in the basket of your air fryer and cook for 5 minutes at 390°F.
3. Serve as an appetizer by arranging them on a dish.

Nutrition per serving: *Calories: 162; Fat: 6g; Protein: 14g; Carbs: 8g; Fiber: 4g.*

15. Roasted Pepper Rolls

Prep Time: 20 Minutes / Cooking Time: 10 Minutes/ Total Time: 30 Minutes / Yield: 8 Servings.

Ingredients:
4 oz. feta cheese; crumbled
1 yellow bell pepper; halved
1 green onion; chopped
2 tbsp. oregano; chopped.
Salt and black pepper to the taste
1 orange bell pepper; halved.

Direction:
1. In a mixing bowl, whisk together the cheese, onion, oregano, salt, and pepper.

2. Place bell pepper halves in the basket of your air fryer and cook for 10 minutes at 400°F, then transfer to a chopping board, cool, and peel.

3. Divide the cheese mixture among the bell pepper halves, roll them up, secure with toothpicks, and serve as an appetizer.

Nutrition per serving: *Calories: 170; Fat: 1g; Protein: 5g; Carbs: 8g; Fiber: 2g.*

CHAPTER 6: Dinner Recipes

1. Garlic Herb Turkey Breast

Prep time: 1 Hour / Cooking Time: 40 Minutes/ Total time: 1Hour & 40 minutes / Yield: 6 Servings.

Ingredients:
4 tbsps. butter, melted
2 lbs. turkey breast
1 tsp. thyme
3 cloves garlic
1 tsp. rosemary

Directions:
1. Preheat the Air Fryer to 375°F.
2. Pat the turkey breast dry with a paper towel. Garlic should be minced, while rosemary and thyme should be chopped.
3. In a small mixing dish, melt the butter and combine it with the garlic, thyme, and rosemary. Butter the turkey breasts and place them on a plate.
4. Cook for 40 minutes, skin side up, in the Air Fryer basket, or until internal temperature reaches 160° F, flipping halfway through.
5. Allow for a 5-minute cooling period before serving.

Nutrition per serving: *Calories: 321; Fat: 19.29g; Protein: 34.35g; Carbohydrates: 0.56g*

2. Honey-Lime Chicken Wings

Prep time: 20 minutes / Cooking Time: 30 Minutes/ Total time: 50 minutes / Yield: 4 Servings.

Ingredients:
2 tbsps. lime juice
2 lbs. chicken wings
0.25 cup honey
1 garlic clove, pressed

1 tbsp. lime zest

Directions:

1. Preheat the Air Fryer to 360 degrees Fahrenheit.
2. Combine the garlic, honey, lime juice, and zest in a mixing bowl. Toss in the wings and coat them in the sauce.
3. Make the wings one at a time. Cook for 25-30 minutes, or until crisp. At 8-minute intervals, shake the basket.
4. Garnish and serve as desired.

Nutrition per serving: *Calories: 375; Fat: 9.56g; Protein: 51.60g; Carbohydrates: 18.6g*

3. Rotisserie-Style, Whole Chicken

Prep time: 50 minutes / Cooking Time: 30 Minutes/ Total time: 45 minutes / Yield: 4 Servings.

Ingredients:

2 tsps. olive oil, as needed
6-7 lb. whole chicken
1 tbsp. salt, seasoned

Directions:

1. Preheat the Air Fryer to 350 degrees Fahrenheit.
2. Brush the chicken with oil and season with salt.
3. Place the chicken skin-side down in the Air Fryer.
4. Allow 30 minutes for cooking. Turn the chicken over and cook for another 30 minutes in the air fryer.
5. Allow for a ten-minute cooling period before slicing.
6. **Note:** This recipe is for a 3.7-quart Air Fryer and chickens weighing less than lbs.

Nutrition per serving: *Calories: 859; Fat: 9.56g; Protein: 151.44g; Carbohydrates: 0g*

4. Chicken Curry

Prep Time: 1 Hr. & 10 Mins / Cooking Time: 25 Minutes/ Total Time: 1 Hr. & 35 Mins /Yield: 7 Servings

Ingredients:
1 onion, minced
1 tbsp. coconut oil
2 cloves garlic, crushed and minced
2 tbsps. white sugar
8 oz. tomato sauce, canned
3 tbsps. curry powder
14 oz. tomatoes, canned and diced
½ cup chicken broth
2 lbs. chicken breast fillet
14 oz. milk, skimmed
Salt and pepper to taste

Directions:
1. In your Instant Pot, select the sauté function.
2. Add the coconut oil to the mixture.
3. Cook for 2 minutes with the onion and garlic.
4. Add the curry powder and whisk to combine.
5. Select "Cancel" from the drop-down menu.
6. Combine the sugar, tomato sauce, tomatoes, and chicken broth in a large mixing bowl. Stir.
7. Season the chicken with salt and pepper on both sides.
8. Put the chicken in the pot and cover it with water.
9. Make sure the pot is secure.
10. Cook for 10 minutes on high.
11. Allow for a natural release of pressure.
12. Return the chicken to the pot after shredding it.
13. Select the sauté option.
14. Cook for a total of 3 minutes.
15. Add the skimmed milk to the mixture.
16. Cook for another 10 minutes.

Nutrition per serving: *Calories: 563.3; Sat Fat: 23g; Total Fat: 30.3g; Protein: 15.9g; Carbohydrates: 21.5g; Sodium: 766.2mg; Cholesterol: 130mg; Fiber: 4.9g; Sugars: 12.5g; Potassium: 1038g*

5. Lemon Chicken Breast

Prep Time: 10 Minutes / Cooking Time: 30 Minutes/ Total Time: 40 Minutes / Yield: 7 Servings.

Ingredients:
1 tbsp. lemon zest, grated
¼ cup olive oil
1 lemon, sliced
3 tbsps. garlic, minced
⅓ cup dry white wine
2 tbsps. lemon juice
1 tsp. thyme leaves, minced
1 and ½ tsps. oregano, dried and crushed
Salt and pepper to taste
4 chicken breasts, skin-on boneless

Directions:
1. In a baking dish, combine all of the stated ingredients, then add the chicken breasts and coat them thoroughly.
2. Garnish with lemon slices.
3. Toss the toasted bread slices with the mustard mixture.
4. Select "Air Fry" mode on your Air Fryer by pressing the "Power Button."
5. Set the timer to 30 minutes by pressing the Time Button.
6. Press the Temp Button and adjust the temperature to 370°F.
7. Turn on the gadget by pressing the "Start/Pause" button.
8. Place the pan in the Air Frye's Cooking Basket and cook until the pan is done.
9. Finally, serve and enjoy!

Nutrition per serving: *Calories: 337.9; Sat Fat: 1g; Total Fat: 8g; Protein: 12.9g; Carbohydrates: 8g; Sodium: 399mg; Fiber: 1g.*

6. Lemon and Chicken Pepper

Prep Time: 10 Minutes / Cooking Time: 15 Minutes/ Total Time: 25 Minutes / Yield: 4 Servings.

Ingredients:
2 lemon, juiced and rind reserved
Salt and pepper to taste
chicken seasoning
1 tsp. garlic puree
1 chicken breast
Handful peppercorns

Directions:
1. Set your fryer to "AIR FRY" mode and preheat to 352°F.
2. Working on top of a huge piece of silver foil, combine all of the ingredients with the lemon rind.
3. Place the chicken breast on a cutting board and trim away any excess fat and small bones.
4. Season each side with salt and pepper.
5. Season both sides of the chicken with the seasoning.
6. Rub your silver foil sheet with it.
7. Tightly close it.
8. Roll it out flat with a rolling pin.
9. Cook for 15 minutes in your fryer, or until the center is fully done.
10. Serve and enjoy!

Nutrition per serving: *Calories: 350; Sat Fat: 9g; Fat: 33g; Protein: 33g; Carbohydrates: 2g; Sodium: 330mg; Fiber: 1g.*

7. Chicken Curry on Edamame and Asparagus

Prep Time: 10 Minutes / Cooking Time: 10 Minutes/ Total Time: 20 Minutes / Yield: 4 Servings.

Ingredients:
2 cups water
12 oz. chicken breast, boneless and skinless
¼ tsp. black pepper
1 tsp. cumin, ground
¼ cup light mayonnaise

¼ cup plain Greek yogurt

1-½ tsps. curry powder

½ tsp. salt

1 tbsp. sugar

2 cups cut asparagus

1 cup edamame, shelled and thawed

¼ cup green onion or cilantro, chopped

4 cups baby kale mix

½ cup red onion, chopped

Directions:

1. Season the chicken with pepper and cumin and air fry for 6 minutes.

Allow the pressure to naturally release before removing the cover and removing the chicken.

2. Keep it on the cutting board for 5 minutes, then shred it and set it away.

3. In a mixing bowl, combine the mayonnaise, yogurt, salt, curd, and sugar.

4. Cook for 1 minute with the edamame and asparagus in the pot.

5. Remove the asparagus mixture from the colander and release the pressure. Drain well after running it under cold water.

6. Divide the kale mixture evenly among four dishes. Then top with the asparagus mixture.

7. Toss the onions and chicken with the yogurt mixture to coat thoroughly.

8. Spoon equal amounts of asparagus mixture over each plate and top with cilantro.

Nutrition per serving: Calories: 253.1; Total Fat: 9g; Protein: 26g; Carbohydrates: 17g; Fiber: 5g.

8. Quick and Easy Rib Eye Steak

Prep Time: 40 Minutes / Cooking Time: 35 Minutes/ Total Time: 1. Hr & 15 Mins / Yield: 2 Servings.

Ingredients:
1 tbsp. olive oil
2 lbs. steak, unchilled
Steak Rub: salt and pepper mix, as desired Baking pan also needed to fit into the basket

Directions:
1. Select the French Fries icon by pressing the "M" button. Set the timer for four minutes at 400 degrees F.
2. Rub the oil and seasonings into the steak. Air-fry the steak for 14 minutes after placing it in the basket. (After seven minutes, flip it over.)
3. Transfer the rib eye to a dish and let aside for ten minutes to rest.
4. Slice it and garnish it as desired.

Nutrition per serving: Calories: 350; Fat: 55.80g; Protein: 129.44g.

9. Roast Beef

Prep Time: 1 Hour / Cooking Time: 55 Minutes/ Total Time: 1. Hr. & 55 Minutes / Yield: 6 Servings.

Ingredients:
2 lbs. round roast
0.5 tsp. garlic powder
0.5 tsp. oregano
1 tsp. thyme, dried
1 tbsp. Olive oil

Directions:
1. Preheat the Air Fryer to 330 degrees Fahrenheit.
2. Mix the spices together. Brush the steak with oil and spread the spice mixture all over it.

3. Transfer to a baking dish and cook for 30 minutes in the Air Fryer basket. Cook for another 25 minutes on the other side.
4. Allow a few minutes to pass before slicing.
5. Serve with a wonderful side dish and your choice of bread.

Nutrition per serving: *Calories: 286.8; Fat: 10.01g; Protein: 45.9g; Carbohydrates: 0.28g*

10. Air Fryer Chicken Wings

Prep Time: 5 Minutes / Cooking Time: 20 Minutes/ Total Time: 25 Minutes / Yield: 4 Servings.

Ingredients:
1 tbsp. grainy mustard
1 lb. chicken wings
2 cloves garlic, finely minced
Juice of ½ lemon
1 tbsp. shallots, finely minced
2 tsps. fresh thyme leaves, chopped, plus more for garnish
2 tsps. fresh rosemary, chopped
kosher salt
Lemon slices, for serving
Freshly ground black pepper

Directions:
1. Remove the chicken wing portions from the refrigerator and pat them dry (you'll get a crispy wing skin if you remove as much moisture as possible).
2. In a small bowl or baking dish, combine sea salt, black pepper, smoked paprika, garlic powder, onion powder, and baking powder.
3. Toss the spice mixture over the wings to evenly coat them.
4. Arrange the wings in the basket to cook. This basket is known as the "Cook & Crisp" basket in Ninja Foodie.
5. Drizzle olive oil over the chicken wings.

6. Cook the wings for 14 minutes on each side in an air fryer set to 400°F using the Air Crisp option.

7. Serve and enjoy some hot wings.

Nutrition per serving: *Calories: 32; Fat: 1.73g; Protein: 2g; Carbohydrates: 2.55g*

11. Parmesan Chicken Meatballs

Prep Time: 10 Minutes / Cooking Time: 12 Minutes/ Total Time: 22 Minutes / Yield: 4 Servings.

Ingredients:
1-lb. ground chicken
1 large egg, beaten
½ cup Parmesan cheese, grated
½ cup pork rinds, ground
1 tsp. garlic powder
1 tsp. paprika
1 tsp. kosher salt
½ tsp. pepper

Crust:
½ cup pork rinds, ground

Directions:
1. Combine all of the meatball ingredients in a mixing bowl and well combine. Form small meatballs from the ingredients and coat them in pig rinds.

2. Place the meatballs in the air fryer basket, coated side up. To select the "Bake" mode, press the "Power Button" on the Air Fry Oven and spin the dial.

3. To adjust the cooking duration to 12 minutes, press the "Time" button and then turn the dial again. To set the temperature, press the Temp button and rotate the dial to 400oF.

4. Once the oven has hot, insert the air fryer basket and close the lid.

5. Serve warm and enjoy.

Nutrition per serving: Calories: 529; Fat: 17g; Protein: 41g; Carbs: 55g

12. Hamburger Soup

Prep Time: 1. Hr & 10 Mins/ Cooking Time: 15 Minutes/ Total Time: 1. Hr & 25 Mins / Yield: 8 Servings.

Ingredients:

1 onion, chopped
45 oz. beef consommé, canned
10 oz. tomato soup, canned
1 ½lb. ground beef
28 oz. tomatoes, canned and diced
½ tsp. thyme, dried
2 cups water
3 stalks celery, chopped
4 carrots, chopped
4 tbsps. pearl barley
1 bay leaf

Directions:

1. In your Instant Pot, select the sauté setting.
2. Add the beef and onion.
3. Cook, stirring often, for 10 minutes.
4. Combine the remaining ingredients in a mixing bowl.
5. Tighten the lid.
6. Select the soup temperature.
7. Allow 30 minutes for cooking.
8. Allow the pressure to naturally release.
9. Remove the bay leaf before serving.

Nutrition per serving: Calories: 251; Sat Fat: 4.3g; Fat: 11.2g; Protein: 18.9g; Carbohydrates: 17.77g; Sodium: 950.4mg; Cholesterol: 51mg; Sugars: 7.7g; Potassium: 660.6mg; Fiber: 3.4g

13. Pot Roast with Veggies

Prep Time: 1. Hr & 40 Mins/ Cooking Time: 15 Minutes/ Total Time: 1. Hr & 10 Mins / Yield: 8 Servings.

Ingredients:
4 tbsps. olive oil, divided
3 lbs. beef chuck roast
2 cups low-sodium beef broth
1 onion, sliced into wedges
1 packet dry onion soup mix
1 ½cups baby carrots
1-lb. baby potatoes
2 ½tbsps. cornstarch mixed with ¼ cup water
Pepper to taste
1 ½tsps. garlic salt

Directions:
1. In your Instant Pot, select the sauté setting.
2. Fill the pot halfway with oil.
3. Cook for 4 minutes per side on the chuck roast.
4. Add the broth to the pot.
5. Combine the oil, onion, onion soup mix, carrots, and potatoes in a mixing dish.
6. Pour the contents of the bowl into the pot.
7. Put the lid on the saucepan.
8. Cook for 1 hour on high.
9. Quickly release the pressure.
10. Place the roast on a dish.
11. Select the sauté option.
12. Stir together the cornstarch and water in the pot.
13. Continue to cook for another 3 minutes.
14. Add the pepper and garlic salt to the sauce.

15. Arrange the vegetables and sauce on top of the roast and serve.

Nutrition per serving: *Calories: 323.2; Sat Fat: 4.4g; Fat: 15.5g; Protein: 25.7; Carbohydrates: 19; Sodium: 1005.4mg; Cholesterol: 78.8mg; Sugars: 2.4g; Potassium: 587.2mg; Fiber: 2.6g*

14. Chicken Drumsticks

Prep Time: 10 Minutes / Cooking Time: 20 Minutes/ Total Time: 30 Minutes / Yield: 8 Servings.

Ingredients:
8 chicken drumsticks
2 tbsps. olive oil
1 tsp. salt
1 tsp. pepper
1 tsp. garlic powder
1 tsp. paprika
½ tsp. cumin

Directions:
1. In a bowl, combine olive oil, salt, black pepper, garlic powder, paprika, and cumin.
2. Using your hands, liberally coat all of the drumsticks in this mixture.
3. Arrange the drumsticks in the Air Fryer basket.
4. Select the "Air Fry" mode by turning the dial.
5. Use the dial to set the cooking time to 20 minutes after pressing the Time button.
6. To set the temperature, press the Temp button and adjust the dial to 375oF.
7. Once the oven is hot, place the Air fryer basket inside.
8. Halfway through cooking, flip the drumsticks.
9. Continue air frying for the remaining 10 minutes.
10. Serve warm.

Nutrition per serving: *Calories: 212; Fat: 11.8g; Protein: 17.3g; Carbs: 14.6g*

15. Sweet and Spicy Montreal Steak

Prep Time: 30 Minutes / Cooking Time: 6 Minutes/ Total Time: 36 Minutes / Yield: 2 Servings

Ingredients:
2 sirloin steaks, boneless
1 tbsp. brown sugar
1 tbsp. Montreal steak seasoning
1 tsp. red pepper, crushed
1 tbsp. olive oil

Directions:
1. Preheat the Air Fryer to 390 degrees Fahrenheit.
2. Brush the steaks with oil, then rub them with the seasonings of your choice.
3. Arrange the steaks in the basket and set the timer for 3 minutes.
4. Flip the steak over and cook for another 3 minutes in the air fryer.
5. Allow to cool before slicing into strips.

Nutrition per serving: *Calories: 1253; Fat: 76g; Protein: 126.3g; Carbohydrates: 6.58g.*

CHAPTER 7: Dessert Recipes

1. French Toast Bites

Prep time: 5 minutes / Cooking Time: 15 Minutes/ Total time: 20 minutes / Yield: 8 Servings.

Ingredients:
Cinnamon
Sweetener
Almond milk
4 pieces wheat bread
3 eggs

Directions:
1. Preheat the air fryer oven to 360ºF.
2. Whisk eggs and thin out with almond milk.
3. 13 cup sweetener plus a generous amount of cinnamon
4. Tear the bread in half, then roll the pieces into a ball and press them together.
5. Soak bread balls in egg, then roll them in cinnamon sugar, ensuring sure they are coated.
6. Bake the coated bread balls in the air fryer for 15 minutes.
7. Serve and enjoy.

Nutrition per serving: *Calories: 289; Fat: 10.9g; Protein: 0g; Carbs: 17g.*

2. Chocolate Donuts

Prep time: 5 minutes / Cooking Time: 20 Minutes/ Total time: 25 minutes / Yield: 9-10 Servings.

Ingredients:
Cooking oil
8oz. can jumbo biscuits
Chocolate sauce, such as Hershey's

Directions:

1. Cut the biscuit dough into eight pieces and arrange them on a level work surface.

Cut a hole in the center of each biscuit with a small circular cookie cutter or a biscuit cutter. You can also use a knife to cut the holes.

2. Cooking oil should be used to grease the basket.

3. In the air fryer oven, place 4 donuts. Do not stack the items. Cook for 4 minutes after spraying with cooking oil.

4. Remove the donuts from the air fryer and flip them. Cook for a further 4 minutes.

5. Take the cooked doughnuts out of the air fryer and repeat with the remaining 4 donuts.

6. Drizzle chocolate sauce on top of the doughnuts and eat while they're still warm.

Nutrition per serving: *Calories: 181; Fat: 98.1g; Protein: 3g; Carbs: 42g.*

3. Carrot Cake

Prep time: 55 minutes / Cooking Time: 45 Minutes/ Total time: 1 Hour & 40 minutes / Yield: 6-7 Servings.

Ingredients:

Cooking spray
1 egg
5 oz. flour
¾ tbsp. baking powder
½ tbsp. baking soda
½ tbsp. cinnamon powder
¼ tbsp. nutmeg
3 tbsps. yogurt
½ cup sugar
¼ cup pineapple juice
½ tbsp. allspice

4 tbsps. sunflower oil
⅓ cup carrots
⅓ cup pecans
⅓ cup coconut flakes

Directions:

1. Combine flour, baking powder, salt, baking soda, allspice, nutmeg, and cinnamon in a mixing bowl and turn.
2. In a separate dish, whisk together the egg, yogurt, oil, sugar, pineapple juice, carrots, coconut flakes, and pecans and turn thoroughly.
3. Blend the two mixtures thoroughly, then pour into a spring form pan sprayed with cooking spray, place in the air fryer, and cook for 45 minutes at 320°F.
4. Allow to cool before slicing and serving.

Nutrition per serving: *Calories: 301; Fat: 16.9g; Protein: 5g; Carbs: 34.1g.*

4. Air Fried Apples

Prep time: 27 minutes / Cooking Time: 17 Minutes/ Total time: 44 minutes / Yield: 4 Servings.

Ingredients:

Raw honey
4 big apples
A handful raisins
1 tbsp. cinnamon

Directions:

1. Spray each apple with cinnamon and honey, then infuse with raisins.
2. Place them in the air fryer and cook for 17 minutes at 367°F.
3. Allow to cool, then serve.

Nutrition per serving: Calories: 100; Fat: 0.33g; Protein: 0.56g; Carbs: 26.8g.

5. Berries Mix

Prep time: 11 minutes / Cooking Time: 6 Minutes/ Total time: 17 minutes / Yield: 4 Servings.

Ingredients:
1 tbsp. Olive oil
2 tbsp. lemon juice
1-½ tbsps. maple syrup
¼ cup basil leaves
1-½ tbsps. champagne vinegar
1 lb. (453.592g) strawberries
1-½ cups blueberries

Directions:
1. Mix in lemon juice with vinegar and maple syrup in a pan, boil over medium heat, put oil, strawberries, and blueberries.
2. Put the mix in the air fryer and cook at 310°F for 6 minutes.
3. Dust basil over, then serve.

Nutrition per serving: Calories: 131; Fat: 3.93g; Protein: 1.3g; Carbs: 26.8g.

6. Mini Cheesecakes

Prep time: 15 minutes / Cooking Time: 10 Minutes/ Total time: 25 minutes / Yield: 2 Servings.

Ingredients:
2 eggs
¾ cup erythritol
2 tbsps. greek yogurt
1 tsp. vanilla extract
½ tsp. fresh lemon juice
16 oz. cream cheese, skimmed and softened

Directions:
1. Combine the erythritol, eggs, vanilla extract, and lemon juice in a blender.
2. Pulse until the mixture is completely smooth. Combine the cream cheese and Greek yogurt in a food processor and process until smooth.
Fill 2 (4-inch) springform pans halfway with the mixture. Select the "air fry" mode by pressing the "power button" on the air fry oven and turning the dial.
To adjust the cooking time to 10 minutes, press the time button again and turn the dial. Set the temperature to 350oF by pressing the temperature button and rotating the dial.
3. To begin, click the "start/pause" button. When the machine beeps to indicate that the oven has been preheated.
4. Place the pans in an "air fry basket" and place in the oven to cook.

Nutrition per serving: *Calories: 886; Fat: 85.8g; Protein: 23g; Carbs: 7.2g; Sugar 1.1g; Cholesterol: 418mg.*

7. Fruity Crumble

Prep time: 15 minutes / Cooking Time: 20 Minutes/ Total time: 35 minutes / Yield: 4 Servings.

Ingredients:
1 tbsp. fresh lemon juice
½ lb. (226.8g) fresh apricots, pitted and cubed 1 cup fresh blackberries
¼ cup chilled margarine, cubed
⅓ cup sugar, divided
cup flour
1 tbsp. cold water
Pinch salt

Directions:
1. Firstly, grease a baking pan.

2. Combine apricots, blackberries, 2 tablespoons sugar, and lemon juice in a large mixing dish.
3. Pour the apricot mixture into the baking pan that has been prepared.
4. Combine the flour, remaining sugar, salt, water, and margarine in a separate dish and mix until a crumbly mixture form.
5. Evenly distribute the flour mixture over the apricot mixture.
6. Press the air fry oven's "power button" and flip the dial to "air fry" mode.
7. Set the cooking time to 20 minutes by pressing the time button and turning the dial again.
8. Now press the temperature button and rotate the dial to 390390ºF.
9. To begin, press the "start/pause" button.
10. Open the lid when the machine beeps to indicate that it has warmed.
11. Place the pan in the oven with the "air fry basket" in place.
12. Allow the pan to cool for 10-15 minutes on a wire rack before serving.

Nutrition per serving: *Calories: 307; Sat Fat: 7.4g; Total Fat: 12.2g; Protein: 4.2; Total Carbs: 47.3g; Fiber: 3.8g; Sodium: 123mg; Cholesterol: 32mg; Sugar: 23.6g.*

8. Air Fried Banana with Sesame Seeds

Prep time: 15 minutes / Cooking Time: 10 Minutes/ Total time: 25 minutes / Yield: 5 Servings.

Ingredients:
5 bananas, sliced
1 tsp. salt
3 tbsps. sesame seeds

1 cup water
1 tsp. baking powder
½ cups flour
½ tbsp. sugar
2 eggs, beaten.

Directions:
1. Preheat the air fryer to 340°F on the bake setting.
2. Combine salt, sesame seeds, flour, baking powder, eggs, sugar, and water in a mixing dish. Coat the sliced bananas in the flour mixture; place in the air fryer basket and cook for 8-10 minutes.
3. Serve and enjoy while chilled.

Nutrition per serving: Calories: 327; Fat: 7.55g; Protein: 9.73g; Carbs: 57.4g.

9. Berry Crumble with Lemon

Prep time: 30 minutes / Cooking Time: 20 Minutes/ Total time: 50 minutes / Yield: 6 Servings.

Ingredients:
5 oz. fresh blueberries
12 oz. fresh strawberries
7 oz. fresh raspberries
5 tbsps. cold margarine
2 tbsps. lemon juice
½ cup sugar
1 tbsp. water
1 cup flour
A pinch salt

Directions:
1. Gently mix the berries together, but leave some chunks. Combine the lemon juice and 2 tbsp. sugar in a mixing bowl.
2. Spread the berry mixture on the bottom of a round cake that has been prepared.

In a mixing dish, combine the flour, salt, and sugar. Pour in the water and knead the margarine with your fingertips until it crumbles.

3. Arrange the berries on top of the crisp batter. Preheat the fryer to 390°F and bake for 20 minutes.

4. Serve and enjoy while chilled.

Nutrition per serving: *Calories: 250; Fat: 10.3g; Protein: 3.3g; Carbs: 37.9g.*

10. Pan-Fried Bananas

Prep time: 15 minutes / Cooking Time: 8 Minutes/ Total time: 23 minutes / Yield: 7-8 Servings.

Preparation Time: 15 minutes

Ingredients:
1 egg white
8 bananas
3 tbsps. corn flour
3 tbsps. vegetable oil
¾ cup breadcrumbs

Directions:
1. Preheat the air fryer to 350°F on the toast setting. In a mixing bowl, combine the oil and breadcrumbs. Coat the bananas in corn flour, then coat them with egg white before dipping them in the breadcrumb mixture.

2. Arrange on a baking sheet lined and bake for 8-12 minutes.

3. Serve and enjoy.

Nutrition per serving: *Calories: 162; Fat: 5.6g; Protein: 1.96g; Carbs: 29g.*

11. Blueberry Pudding

Prep time: 35 minutes / Cooking Time: 25 Minutes/ Total time: 1 Hour/ Yield: 6 Servings.

Ingredients:
2 cups flour
2 cups rolled oats
8 cups blueberries
1 stick margarine
1 cup walnuts
3 tbsps. Maple syrup
2 tbsps. Rosemary

Directions:
1. Spray a baking pan with blueberries and set aside.
2. Combine rolled oats, walnuts, flour, margarine, rosemary, and maple syrup in a mixing bowl, blend well, then spread over blueberries in an air fryer at 350°F for 25 minutes.
3. Allow to cool, then slice and serve.

Nutrition per serving: Calories: 778; Fat: 27.75g; Protein: 14.1g; Carbs: 136.4g.

12. Ricotta Cheesecake

Prep time: 15 minutes / Cooking Time: 25 Minutes/ Total time: 40 minutes / Yield: 8 Servings.

Ingredients:
3 eggs
17.6 oz. Ricotta cheese
¾ cup sugar
1 tbsp. fresh lemon juice
3 tbsps. corn starch
2 tsps. vanilla extract
1 tsp. fresh lemon zest, finely grated

Directions:
1. Combine all ingredients in a large mixing basin and stir until well blended.

Fill a baking pan with the mixture. To select the "air fry" mode, press the "power button" on the air fry oven and spin the dial.

2. Set the cooking time to 25 minutes by pressing the time button and turning the dial again. To set the temperature, press the temp button and crank the dial to 320oF. To begin, press the "start/pause" button.

Open the lid when the machine beeps to indicate that it has preheated.

Place the pan in the oven with the "air fry basket" in place.

Allow the cake pan to cool completely on a wire rack.

3. Refrigerate for at least 12 hours before serving.

Nutrition per serving: *Calories: 197; Fat: 6.6g; Protein: 9.2g; Carbs: 25.6g; Sugar: 19.4g; Cholesterol: 81mg.*

13. Cherry Clafoutis

Prep time: 15 minutes / Cooking Time: 25 Minutes/ Total time: 40 minutes / Yield: 4 Servings.

Ingredients:
1 egg
1 ½ cups fresh cherries, pitted
2 tbsps. sugar
3 tbsps. vodka
¼ cup flour
Pinch salt
½ cup sour cream
1 tbsp. margarine
¼ cup powdered sugar

Directions:
1. Combine the cherries and vodka in a mixing dish.
2. Combine the flour, sugar, and salt in a separate bowl.
3. Mix in the sour cream and egg until a smooth dough is formed.

4. Grease and flour a cake pan.
5. Evenly distribute the flour mixture in the prepared cake pan.
6. Cover the dough with the cherry mixture.
7. Make a dot pattern with margarine on top.
8. Select the "air fry" mode by pressing the "power button" on the air fry oven and turning the dial.
9. Set the cooking time to 25 minutes by pressing the time button and turning the dial again.
10. Press the temperature button and turn the dial to 355ºF.
11. To begin, press the "start/pause" button.
12. Open the lid when the unit beeps to indicate that it is preheated.
13. Place the pan in the oven with the "air fry basket" in place.
14. Allow the pan to cool for 10–15 minutes before serving on a wire rack.
15. Place the clafoutis on a serving plate and dust with powdered sugar.
16. Serve the clafoutis warm, cut into desired size slices.

Nutrition per serving: *Calories: 241; Sat Fat: 5.9g; Protein: 3.9g; Total Fat: 10.1g; Total Carbs: 29.1g; Fiber: 1.3g; Sodium: 90 mg; Cholesterol: 61mg; Sugar: 20.6g.*

14. Apple Treat with Raisins

Prep time: 15 minutes / Cooking Time: 10 Minutes/ Total time: 25 minutes / Yield: 4 Servings.

Ingredients:
1 ½ oz. almonds
4 apples, cored
2 tbsps. Sugar
¾ oz. raisins.

Directions:
1. Preheat the air fryer to 360°F and combine the sugar, almonds, and raisins in a mixing bowl.
2. Using a hand blender, combine the ingredients.
3. Spoon the almond mixture into the cored apples.
4. Cook for 10 minutes in your air fryer basket with the prepped apples.
5. Top with powdered sugar before serving.

Nutrition per serving: Calories: 188; Fat: 27.75g; Protein: 2.88g; Carbs: 35.63g.

15. Cinnamon & Honey Apples with Hazelnuts

Prep time: 13 minutes / Cooking Time: 10 Minutes/ Total time: 23 minutes / Yield: 2 Servings.

Ingredients:
4 apples
1 oz. margarine
2 oz. mixed seeds
2 oz. breadcrumbs
2 tbsp. hazelnuts, chopped
1 tsp. cinnamon
Zest of 1 orange
2 tbsp. honey.

Directions:
1. Preheat the air fryer to 350ºF and core the apples.
To keep their skin from separating, score it as well.
2. In a bowl, mix up the remaining ingredients; stuff the apples with the mixture and bake for 10 minutes.
3. Garnish with chopped hazelnuts before serving.

Nutrition per serving: Calories: 1174; Fat: 82.5g; Protein: 22.7g; Carbs: 106.1g.

CHAPTER 8: Vegetarian Recipes

1. Parmesan Broccoli and Asparagus

Prep Time: 20 Minutes / Cooking Time: 15 Minutes/ Total Time: 25 Minutes / Yield: 4 Servings

Preparation Time: 20 minutes

Ingredients:
½ lb. asparagus, trimmed
1 broccoli head, florets separated
Juice of 1 lime
1 tbsp. parmesan, grated
1 tbsp. olive oil
Salt and black pepper to taste
Directions:
1. Toss the asparagus with the broccoli and all of the other ingredients except the parmesan in a bowl, then transfer to the basket of the air fryer and cook for 15 minutes at 400°F.
2. Divide amongst plates and garnish with parmesan cheese before serving.

Nutrition per serving: *Calories: 172; Fat: 5g; Protein: 9g; Carbs: 4g*

2. Endives with Bacon Mix

Prep Time: 15 Minutes / Cooking Time: 15 Minutes/ Total Time: 30 Minutes / Yield: 3-4 Servings.

Ingredients:
4Endives, trimmed and halved
Salt and black pepper to taste
1 tbsp. olive oil
2 tbsps. bacon, cooked and crumbled
½ tsp. nutmeg, ground

Directions:
1. Place the endives in the basket of the air fryer and season with salt and pepper to taste, as well as the oil and nutmeg; mix gently.
2. Preheat oven to 360°F and bake for 10 minutes.
3. Arrange the endives on different dishes, then top with the bacon and serve.

Nutrition per serving: Calories: 151; Fat: 6g; Protein: 6g; Carbs: 14g; Fiber: 8g

3. Flatbread

Prep Time: 5 Minutes / Cooking Time: 7 Minutes/ Total Time: 13 Minutes / Yield: 2 Servings.

Ingredients:
1 cup mozzarella cheese, shredded
¼ cup almond flour
1-oz. full-fat cream cheese, softened

Directions:
1. Microwave for 30 seconds to melt the mozzarella. Blend in the almond flour until it's completely smooth.
2. Mix in the cream cheese. Continue to combine until a dough has formed. If necessary, knead with damp hands.
3. Divide the dough into two parts and spread out to a thickness of 14 inches between two sheets of parchment paper.
4. Line the air fryer basket with parchment paper and set the flatbreads inside. If necessary, work in batches.
5. Bake for 7 minutes at 320°F. At the halfway point, flip once more.
6. Finally, serve and enjoy.

Nutrition per serving: Calories: 296; Fat: 22.6g; Protein: 6g; Carbs: 3.3g

4. Creamy Potatoes

Prep Time: 10 Minutes / Cooking Time: 20 Minutes/ Total Time: 30 Minutes / Yield: 2 Servings.

Ingredients:
¾ lb. Potatoes, peeled and cubed
1 tbsp. olive oil
Salt and black pepper, to taste
½ tbsp. hot paprika
½ cup Greek yogurt

Directions:
1. Place the potatoes in a basin and cover with water. Set aside for 10 minutes. Drain and wipe dry before transferring to a new bowl.
2. Toss the potatoes with salt, pepper, paprika, and half of the oil.
3. Place the potatoes in the air fryer basket and cook for 20 minutes at 360°F.
4. Whisk together the yogurt, salt, pepper, and the remaining oil in a basin.
5. Arrange potatoes on plates, drizzle with yogurt dressing, and serve.

Nutrition per serving: *Calories: 170; Fat: 2.9g; Protein: 5g; Carb: 20g*

5. Crispy Brussels Sprouts and Potatoes

Prep Time: 10 Minutes / Cooking Time: 8 Minutes/ Total Time: 18 Minutes / Yield: 2 Servings.

Ingredients:
¾ lb. brussels sprouts, washed and trimmed
½ cup new potatoes, chopped
2 tsps. bread crumbs
Salt and black pepper, to taste
2 tsps. butter

Directions:

1. Combine Brussels sprouts, potatoes, bread crumbs, salt, pepper, and butter in a mixing bowl. Mix thoroughly.
2. Place in the air fryer and cook for 8 minutes at 400oF.
3. Serve and enjoy.

Nutrition per serving: *Calories: 152; Fat: 3.1g; Protein: 4g; Carb: 17g*

6. Almond Flour Battered and Crisped Onion Rings

Prep Time: 5 Minutes / Cooking Time: 20 Minutes/ Total Time: 25 Minutes / Yield: 3 Servings.

Ingredients:

½ cup almond flour
¾ cup coconut milk
1 big white onion, sliced into rings
1 egg, beaten
1 tbsp. baking powder
1 tbsp. paprika, smoked
Salt and pepper to taste

Directions:

1. Preheat the air fryer oven to 350 degrees Fahrenheit for 5 minutes.
2. Combine the almond flour, baking powder, smoked paprika, salt, and pepper in a mixing bowl.
3. Whisk together the eggs and coconut milk in a separate dish.
4. Dip the onion slices into the egg mixture and let them soak for a few minutes.
5. Using the almond flour mixture, coat the onion slices.
6. Pour into the rack/basket in the oven. Preheat the oven to 325°F and set the timer for 15 minutes. To begin, select START/STOP. To ensure proper cooking, shake the fryer basket.

Nutrition per serving: Calories: 217; Fat: 17g; Protein: 5g; Carbs: 2g; Fiber: 6g.

7. Crunchy Cauliflower

Prep Time: 20 Minutes / Cooking Time: 15 Minutes/ Total Time: 25 Minutes / Yield: 5 Servings.

Ingredients:
2 oz. cauliflower
1 tbsp. potato starch
1 tsp. olive oil
Salt & pepper to taste

Directions:
1. Preheat the air fryer toaster oven to 400 degrees Fahrenheit for 3 minutes.
Slice the cauliflower into equal pieces and toss with the florets into the bowl if using potato starch.
2. Drizzle in some olive oil and toss to coat.
3. Spray the interior of the air fryer toaster oven basket with olive oil cooking spray, then add the cauliflower.
4. Cook for 8 minutes, then shake the basket and cook for an additional 5 minutes, depending on crispiness desired.
5. Toss the roasted cauliflower with fresh parsley, kosher salt, and your favorite seasonings or sauce.

Nutrition per serving: Calories: 36; Fat: 1g; Protein: 1g; Carbs: 5g; Fiber: 2g.

8. Veg Buffalo Cauliflower

Prep Time: 20 Minutes / Cooking Time: 15 Minutes/ Total Time: 35 Minutes / Yield: 3 Servings.

Ingredients:
1 medium head cauliflower
1 tsp. avocado oil
1 tbsp. red hot sauce

1 tbsp. nutritional yeast
1 ½ tsp. maple syrup
¼ tsp. sea salt
1 tbsp. cornstarch or arrowroot starch

Directions:

1. Preheat your air fryer toaster oven to 360 degrees Fahrenheit. Except for the cauliflower, combine all of the ingredients in a mixing basin. To blend them, stir them together.
2. Add the cauliflower and toss to evenly coat. Cook half of your cauliflower in an air fryer for 15 minutes, shaking continuously, until you achieve the appropriate consistency.
3. Repeat with the remaining cauliflower, but reduce the cooking time to 10 minutes.
4. Refrigerate the cauliflower for 3 to 4 days, properly packed. Return to the air fryer to reheat for 1-2 minutes, or until crisp.

Nutrition per serving: *Calories: 246.3; Fat:19.8g; Protein: 4.1g; Carbs:135g; Fiber: 2g.*

9. Creamy Cabbage

Prep Time: 10 Minutes / Cooking Time:20 Minutes/ Total Time: 30 Minutes / Yield: 7 Servings.

Ingredients:
½ green cabbage head, chopped
½ yellow onion, chopped
Salt and black pepper, to taste
½ cup whipped cream
1 tbsp. cornstarch

Directions:

1. In the air fryer, place the cabbage and onion.
2. Combine cornstarch, cream, salt, and pepper in a mixing bowl. Combine all ingredients in a mixing bowl and pour over cabbage.

3. Toss and bake for 20 minutes at 400°F.
4. Serve and enjoy.

Nutrition per serving: *Calories: 208; Fat: 10g; Protein: 5g; Carbs: 15.9g.*

10. Green Beans and Cherry Tomatoes

Prep Time: 10 Minutes / Cooking Time: 15 Minutes/ Total Time: 25 Minutes / Yield: 2-3 Servings.

Ingredients:
8 oz. cherry tomatoes
8 oz. green beans
1 tbsp. olive oil
Salt and black pepper, to taste

Directions:
1. Toss cherry tomatoes, green beans, olive oil, salt, and pepper together in a mixing bowl.
2. Bake at 400°F for 15 minutes in an air fryer. Give it a good shake.
3. Serve and enjoy.

Nutrition per serving: *Calories: 162; Fat: 6g; Protein: 9.1g; Carbs: 8g.*

11. Asparagus & Parmesan

Prep Time: 10 Minutes / Cooking Time: 6 Minutes/ Total Time: 16 Minutes / Yield: 2 Servings.

Ingredients:
1 tsp. sesame oil
11 oz. asparagus
1 tsp. chicken stock
½ tsp. ground white pepper
3 oz Parmesan

Directions:
1. Roughly cut the asparagus once it has been washed.

2. Combine the chopped asparagus, chicken stock, and freshly ground white pepper in a mixing bowl.
3. Drizzle the sesame oil over the vegetables and shake them.
4. Place the asparagus in the basket of the air fryer.
5. Preheat the oven to 400°F and cook the vegetables for 4 minutes.
6. In the meantime, grate the Parmesan cheese.
7. When the timer goes off, lightly shake the asparagus and top with grated cheese.
8. Cook the asparagus for an additional 2 minutes at 400°F. Transfer the cooked asparagus to the serving plates after that.
10. Serve and enjoy.

Nutrition per serving: *Calories: 189; Fat: 11g; Protein: 17.3g; Carbs: 8g; Fiber: 3.2g.*

12. Chili Squash Wedges

Prep Time: 10 Minutes / Cooking Time: 18 Minutes/ Total Time: 28 Minutes / Yield: 2 Servings.

Ingredients:
11 oz. Acorn squash
½ tsp. salt
1 tbsp. olive oil
½ tsp. chili pepper
½ tsp. paprika

Directions:
1. Cut the acorn squash into wedges for serving.
2. Season the wedges with salt, olive oil, chili powder, and paprika, to taste.
3. Gently massage the wedges.
4. Preheat the air fryer to 400 degrees Fahrenheit.
5. Cook for 18 minutes in the air fryer basket with acorn squash wedges.
6. After 9 minutes of cooking, flip the wedges to the other side.

7. Serve hot and enjoy!

Nutrition per serving: *Calories: 125; Fat: 7.2g; Protein: 1.5g; Carbs: 16.6g; Fiber: 2.7g.*

13. Chard with Cheddar

Prep Time: 10 Minutes / Cooking Time: 11 Minutes/ Total Time: 21 Minutes / Yield: 2 Servings.

Ingredients:
3 oz. Cheddar cheese, grated
10 oz. Swiss chard
3 tbsps. cream
1 tbsp. sesame oil
salt and pepper to taste

Directions:
1. Thoroughly wash Swiss chard and chop it.
2. Season the chopped Swiss chard with salt and freshly ground white pepper.
3. Give it a proper stir.
4. Drizzle the sesame oil over the Swiss chard and toss gently with two spatulas.
5. Preheat the air fryer to 260 degrees Fahrenheit.
6. Cook for 6 minutes in the air fryer basket with chopped Swiss chard.
7. After 3 minutes of cooking, give it a good shake.
8. Pour the cream into the air fryer basket and stir to combine.
9. Cook the food for a further 3 minutes.
Then raise the temperature to 400 degrees Fahrenheit.
11. Add the shredded cheese and cook for an additional 2 minutes.
12. Finally, transfer the meal to serving plates and enjoy.

Nutrition per serving: *Calories: 189; Fat: 11g; Protein: 17.3g; Carbs: 8g; Fiber: 3.2g.*

14. Corn on Cobs

Prep Time: 15 Minutes / Cooking Time: 15 Minutes/ Total Time: 30 Minutes / Yield: 7 Servings.

Preparation Time: 10 minutes
Cooking Time: 10 minutes
Servings: 2
Ingredients:
2 fresh corn on cobs
2 tsps. butter
1 tsp. salt
1 tsp. paprika
¼ tsp. olive oil
Directions:
1. Preheat the air fryer to 400 degrees Fahrenheit.
2. Sprinkle the salt and paprika over the corn on the cobs.
3. Finally, drizzle the olive oil over the corn on the cobs.
4. In the air fryer basket, place the corn on the cobs.
5. Cook the corn for 10 minutes on the cobs.
6. When the time is up, place the corn on the cobs in the serving plates and gently rub with the butter.
7. Immediately serve the food.

Nutrition per serving: *Calories: 122; Fat: 5.5g; Protein: 3.2g; Carbs: 18g; Fiber: 2.4g.*

15. Dill Mashed Potato

Prep Time: 10 Minutes / Cooking Time: 15 Minutes/ Total Time: 25 Minutes / Yield: 2 Servings.

Ingredients:
2 potatoes
2 tbsps. fresh dill, chopped
1 tsp. butter

½ tsp. salt

¼ cup half and half

Directions:

1. Preheat the air fryer to 390 degrees Fahrenheit.
2. Thoroughly rinse the potatoes before placing them in the air fryer.
3. Cook for 15 minutes with the potatoes.
4. Remove the potatoes from the air fryer after that.
5. Wash the potatoes and peel them.
6. Using a fork, thoroughly mash the potatoes.
7. Finally, season with salt and chopped fresh dill.
8. Gently stir in the butter and half-and-half.
9. Using the hand blender, thoroughly blend the mixture.
10. As soon as the mashed potatoes are done, serve and enjoy.

Nutrition per serving: *Calories: 211; Fat:5.7g; Protein: 5.1g; Carbs: 36g; Fiber: 5.6g.*

CHAPTER 9: Seafood Recipes

1. Snapper and Spring Onions

Prep Time: 19 Minutes / Cooking Time: 14 Minutes/ Total Time: 33 Minutes / Yield: 4 Servings.

Ingredients:

4 snapper fillets, boneless and skin scored
6 spring onions, chopped.
Juice of ½ lemon
3 tbsps. olive oil
2 tbsps. sweet paprika
A pinch salt and black pepper

Directions:

1. In a mixing bowl, whisk together the paprika, the remaining ingredients, and the fish.
2. Rub the fish with the mixture, then place the fillets in the basket of your air fryer and cook for 7 minutes on each side at 390°F.
3. Divide among plates and serve with a salad on the side.

Nutrition per serving: *Calories: 241; Fat: 12g; Protein: 13g; Carbs: 6g; Fiber: 4g.*

2. Trout and Zucchinis

Prep Time: 20 Minutes / Cooking Time: 15 Minutes/ Total Time: 35 Minutes / Yield: 4 Servings.

Ingredients:

3 zucchinis, cut in medium chunks
4 trout fillets, boneless
¼ cup tomato sauce
1 garlic clove, minced
½ cup cilantro, chopped
1 tbsp. lemon juice
2 tbsps. olive oil

Salt and black pepper to taste

Directions:

1. Toss the fish with the other ingredients in a pan that fits your air fryer, toss, place in the fryer, and cook at 380°F for 15 minutes.

2. Arrange everything on plates and serve immediately.

Nutrition per serving: Calories: 220; Fat: 12g; Protein: 9.1g; Carbs: 6g; Fiber: 4g.

3. Dill Fish Chops

Prep Time: 10 Minutes / Cooking Time: 11 Minutes/ Total Time: 21 Minutes / Yield: 4 Servings.

Ingredients:

4 (5 oz.) cod fillets, cut into 2-inch cubes
½ cup tapioca starch
2 eggs
1 cup almond flour
1 ½ fish seasoning, dried
1 ½ dill, dried
Salt and black pepper to taste
½ tsp. mustard powder
Olive oil for greasing

Directions:

1. Place the dripping pan in the bottom of the air fryer and preheat for 2 to 3 minutes on Air Fry mode at 390°F.

2. In a shallow dish, pour the tapioca starch; in a larger bowl, whisk the eggs; in another plate, combine the almond flour, fish seasoning, dill, salt, black pepper, and mustard powder.

3. Lightly coat the fish cubes in the starch, then dip them in the eggs and generously coat them in the mustard mixture on all sides.

4. Drizzle a little olive oil over the coated fish and place it in the rotisserie basket. Close the oven and place the basket in it,

using the rotisserie ling. Set the timer for 11 minutes and cook until the outside of the fish is golden brown.

5. Arrange the coated fish on serving plates and top with your chosen sauce while still warm.

Nutrition per serving: Calories: 206; Fat: 4g; Protein: 22.8g; Carbs: 18.2g; Fiber: 0.4g.

4. Delicious Catfish

Prep Time: 10 Minutes / Cooking Time: 20 Minutes/ Total Time: 30 Minutes / Yield: 1 Servings.

Ingredients:
Black pepper and Salt
4 catfish fillets
A pinch sweet paprika
1 tbsp. parsley
1 tbsp. olive oil
1 tbsp. lemon juice

Directions:
1. Season catfish fillets with salt, paprika, and pepper, then sprinkle with olive oil and rub thoroughly. Then place in an air fryer basket and cook for 20 minutes at 400°F. After 10 minutes, turn the fish over.

2. Arrange the fish on plates.

3. Garnish with parsley and a squeeze of lemon juice, then serve and enjoy.

Nutrition per serving: Calories: 247; Fat: 15.7g; Protein: 25g; Carbs: 0.2g; Sodium: 86mg; Fiber: 0.1g; Sugars: 0.1g.

5. Shrimp Scampi

Prep Time: 5 Minutes / Cooking Time: 8 Minutes/ Total Time: 13 Minutes / Yield: 5 Servings.

Ingredients:

1 tbsp. lemon juice
4 tbsps. butter
1 lb. shrimp, defrosted
1 tsp. chives, dried
1 tbsp. fresh basil leaves, minced
2 tbsps. chicken stock
1 tbsp. garlic, minced
2 tsps. red pepper flakes

Directions:
1. In a 6-inch hot pan, melt butter.
2. Cook for 2 minutes with the garlic and red pepper flakes.
3. Place the pan in the air fryer to finish cooking.
4. Toss in the remaining ingredients, excluding the basil, into the pan.
5. Cook for 5 minutes, stirring occasionally.
6. Remove the heated pan from the fryer after thoroughly mixing.
7. Remove the shrimp from the heat and set aside for 1 minute.
8. Gently combine all ingredients and top with basil.
9. Serve and enjoy while it's still warm.

Nutrition per serving: *Calories: 372; Sat Fat: 5.8g; Total Fat: 11.1g; Protein: 63.5g; Carbs: 0.9g; Sodium: 749mg; Fiber: 0.2g; Sugars: 0.2g; Cholesterol: 610mg.*

6. Sesame Seeds Coated Fish

Prep Time: 20 Minutes / Cooking Time: 14 Minutes/ Total Time: 24 Minutes / Yield: 28 Servings.

Preparation Time: 20 minutes

Ingredients:
½ cup sesame seeds, toasted
½ tsp. rosemary, dried and crushed
8 tbsps. olive oil
14 fish fillets, frozen (white fish of your choice) 6 eggs

½ cup breadcrumbs

8 tbsps. plain flour

Salt and freshly ground black pepper, to taste

Directions:

1. In three separate plates, put flour in one, eggs in another, and the remaining ingredients (save the fillets) in the third.
2. Coat the fillets in flour and then dip them in beaten eggs.
3. Then, liberally dredge with the sesame seeds mixture.
4. Preheat the air fryer to 390 degrees Fahrenheit and line the air fryer basket with foil.
5. Arrange the fillets in the basket and cook for 14 minutes, flipping halfway through.
6. Remove from the oven and serve immediately.
7. **Tip:** make use shallow dishes.

Nutrition per serving: Calories: 179; Sat Fat: 1.6g; Total Fat: 9.3g; Protein: 7.7g; Carbs: 15.9g; Sodium: 247mg; Fiber: 1.1g; Sugars: 0.7g; Cholesterol: 53mg; Potassium: 32mg.

7. Simple Salmon

Prep Time: 22 Minutes / Cooking Time: 12 Minutes/ Total Time: 34 Minutes / Yield: 2 Servings.

Ingredients:

2 (4-oz.) salmon fillets, skin removed

1 medium lemon.

2 tbsps. butter, unsalted and melted.

½ tsp. dill, dried

½ tsp. garlic powder.

Directions:

1. Place each fillet on a piece of aluminum foil that is 5 inches square. Garnish with a sprinkling of garlic powder and a drizzle of butter.
2. Remove half of the lemon zest and sprinkle it over the salmon. Cut the remaining half of the lemon in half and place

two slices on each piece of salmon. Dill should be sprinkled over the salmon.

3. To completely close the packets, gather and fold the foil at the top and sides.

Fill the air fryer basket with foil packs. Preheat the oven to 400 degrees Fahrenheit and set the timer for 12 minutes.

4. When thoroughly cooked, the salmon will flake easily and have an internal temperature of at least 145°F.

5. Serve and enjoy.

Nutrition per serving: *Calories: 252; Fat: 15g; Protein: 29.5g; Carbs: 2g; Fiber: 4g.*

8. Salmon and Cauliflower Rice

Prep Time: 30 Minutes / Cooking Time: 25 Minutes/ Total Time: 55 Minutes / Yield: 4 Servings.

Ingredients:
4 salmon fillets, boneless
½ cup chicken stock
1 cup cauliflower, riced
1 tbsp. olive oil
1 tsp. turmeric powder
Salt and black pepper to taste

Directions:
1. Toss the cauliflower rice with the remaining ingredients (except the salmon) in a pan that fits your air fryer.

2. Arrange the salmon fillets on top of the cauliflower rice in the pan, place it in the fryer, and cook for 25 minutes at 360°F, flipping the fish after 15 minutes.

3. Arrange on plates and serve.

Nutrition per serving: *Calories: 241; Fat: 12g; Protein: 12g; Carbs: 6g; Fiber: 2g.*

9. Shrimp and Green Beans

Prep Time: 20 Minutes / Cooking Time: 15 Minutes/ Total Time: 35 Minutes / Yield: 4 Servings.

Ingredients:
½ lb. green beans, trimmed and halved
1 lb. shrimp, peeled and deveined
¼ cup ghee, melted
2 tbsps. cilantro, chopped.
Juice of 1 lime
A pinch of salt and black pepper

Directions:
1. Toss all of the ingredients in a pan that fits your air fryer.
2. Place in the fryer and cook for 15 minutes at 360°F, shaking the fryer halfway through.
3. Serve by dividing the mixture into bowls.

Nutrition per serving: *Calories: 222; Fat: 8g; Protein: 10g; Carbs: 5g; Fiber: 3.1g.*

10. Lemon Tuna

Prep Time: 10 Minutes / Cooking Time: 12 Minutes/ Total Time: 22 Minutes / Yield: 4 Servings.

Ingredients:
1 tbsp. fresh lime juice
1 egg
3 tbsps. canola oil
2 tbsps. hot sauce
2 tsps. Dijon mustard
2 tbsps. fresh parsley, chopped
½ lb. plain tuna, water packed
½ cup breadcrumbs

Salt and freshly ground black pepper, to taste

Directions:

1. In a mixing dish, combine the tuna, parsley, mustard, crumbs, citrus juice, and spicy sauce.
2. In a mixing bowl, combine the oil, salt, and eggs, and form patties from the mixture. Refrigerate.
3. Preheat the air fryer to 360 degrees Fahrenheit.
4. Cook the patties for 12 minutes in the air fryer basket.
5. Remove from the oven and serve immediately.
6. **Tip:** Keep the patties refrigerated for at least 3 hours.

__Nutrition per serving:__ Calories: 315; Sat Fat: 2.1g; Total Fat: 18.7g; Protein: 10.7g; Carbs: 25g; Sodium: 729mg; Fiber: 1.1g; Sugars: 1.2g; Cholesterol: 53mg; Potassium: 79mg.

11. Parsley Catfish

Prep Time: 5 Minutes / Cooking Time: 25 Minutes/ Total Time: 30 Minutes / Yield: 4 Servings.

Ingredients:

4 catfish fillets
¼ cup Louisiana Fish fry
1 tbsp. olive oil
1 tbsp. parsley, chopped (optional)
1 lemon, sliced
Fresh herbs, to garnish

Directions:

1. Preheat the air fryer to 400 degrees Fahrenheit.
2. Rinse and pat the fish fillets before frying.
3. Season the fillets thoroughly with the seasoning.
4. Drizzle oil over each fillet.
5. Place the fillets in the basket of the air fryer.
6. Cook for 10 minutes with the cover on.
7. Cook for another 10 minutes after flipping the fillets.
8. Cook for 3 minutes on the other side, until the fish is crispy.

9. Toss with parsley, fresh herbs, and a squeeze of lemon.
10. Serve warm and enjoy.

Nutrition per serving: Calories: 248; Sat Fat: 2.7g; Total Fat: 15.7g; Protein: 24.9g; Carbs: 0.4g; Sodium: 94mg; Fiber: 0g; Sugars: 0g; Cholesterol: 75mg.

12. Cajun Spiced Salmon

Prep Time: 10 Minutes / Cooking Time: 8 Minutes/ Total Time: 18 Minutes / Yield: 8 Servings.

Ingredients:
4 tbsps. Cajun seasoning
4 salmon steaks

Directions:
1. In a bowl, combine the Cajun seasoning and distribute it evenly over the salmon.
2. Preheat the air fryer to 385 degrees Fahrenheit.
3. Arrange the salmon steaks on the air fryer grill pan.
4. Cook for about 8 minutes, flipping halfway through.
5. Remove from the oven and serve while hot.
6. **Tip:** Before putting salmon steaks in the air fryer, set them aside for at least 15 minutes.

Nutrition per serving: Calories: 118; Sat Fat: 0.8g; Total Fat: 5.5g; Protein: 17.3g; Carbs: 0g; Sodium: 114mg; Fiber: 0g; Sugars: 0g; Cholesterol: 39mg; Potassium: 342mg.

13. Trout and Mint

Prep Time: 21 Minutes / Cooking Time: 16 Minutes/ Total Time: 37 Minutes / Yield: 4 Servings.

Ingredients:
1 avocado, peeled, pitted, and roughly chopped.
4 rainbow trout
⅓ pine nuts
1 cup olive oil+ 3 tbsps.

1 cup parsley, chopped.
3 garlic cloves, minced
½ cup mint, chopped.
Zest of 1 lemon
Juice of 1 lemon
A pinch salt and black pepper

Directions:

1. Pat the trout dry, season with salt and pepper, and rub with 3 tablespoons olive oil.
2. Place the fish in the basket of your air fryer and cook for 8 minutes on each side. Distribute the fish among the dishes and drizzle with half of the lemon juice.
3. Pulse the remaining oil with the remaining lemon juice, parsley, garlic, mint, lemon zest, pine nuts, and avocado in a blender until smooth.
4. Serve the trout with this sauce.

Nutrition per serving: Calories: 240; Fat: 12g; Protein: 9g; Carbs: 6g; Fiber: 4g.

14. Packet Lobster Tail

Prep Time: 27 Minutes / Cooking Time: 12 Minutes/ Total Time: 39 Minutes / Yield: 2 Servings.

Ingredients:

2 (6-oz.) lobster tails, halved
2 tbsps. butter, salted and melted
1 tsp. parsley, dried
½ tsp. Old Bay seasoning
Juice of ½ medium lemon

Directions:

1. Place the 2 halved tails on a sheet of aluminum foil, then drizzle with butter, old Bay seasoning, and lemon juice on top.
2. Completely cover the tails with the foil packages. Place the ingredients in the air fryer basket.

3. Preheat the oven to 375 degrees Fahrenheit and set the timer for 12 minutes.

4. Finish by sprinkling dry parsley on top and serving right away.

Nutrition per serving: *Calories: 234; Fat: 10g; Protein: 1g; Carbs: 7g; Fiber: 1g.*

15. Spicy Shrimp

Prep Time: 5 Minutes / Cooking Time: 5 Minutes/ Total Time: 10 Minutes / Yield: 8 Servings.

Ingredients:
2 tsps. old bay seasoning
1 tsp. cayenne pepper
1 tsp. paprika, smoked
4 tbsps. olive oil
2-lbs. tiger shrimp
Salt, to taste

Directions:
1. In a large mixing basin, combine all of the ingredients and m ix thoroughly.

2. Grease the air fryer basket and preheat the air fryer to 390°F.

3. Cook for around 5 minutes in the air fryer basket with the shrimp.

4. Remove from the oven and serve hot.

Tip: You can top up with chili sauce to enhance its taste.

Nutrition per serving: *Calories: 174; Sat Fat: 1.4g; Total Fat: 8.3g; Protein: 23.8g; Carbs: 0.3g; Sodium: 434mg; Fiber: 0.2g; Sugars: 0.1g; Cholesterol: 221mg; Potassium: 217mg.*

CHAPTER 10: Measurement Conversions

10.1 Volume Equivalents (Liquid)

US STANDARD	STANDARD (OUNCES)	METRIC (APPROXIMATE)
2 tablespoons	1 fl. oz.	30 ml
¼ cup	2 fl. oz.	60 ml
½ cup	4 fl. oz.	120 ml
1 cup	8 fl. oz.	240 ml
1½ cups	12 fl. oz.	355 ml
2 cups or 1 pint	16 fl. oz.	475 ml
4 cups or 1 quart	32 fl. oz.	1 L
1 gallon	128 fl. oz.	4 L

10.2 Volume Equivalents (Dry)

US STANDARD	METRIC (APPROXIMATE)
⅛ teaspoon	0.5 ml
¼ teaspoon	1 ml
½ teaspoon	2 ml
¾ teaspoon	4 mL
1 teaspoon	5 mL
1 tablespoon	15 mL
¼ cup	59 ml
⅓ cup	79 mL
½ cup	118 mL
⅔ cup	156 mL
¾ cup	177 mL
1 cup	235 mL
2 cups or 1 pint	475 mL
3 cups	700 mL
4 cups or 1 quart	1 L

10.3 Weight Equivalents

US STANDARD	METRIC (APPROXIMATE)
½ ounce	15 g
2 ounces	60 g
1 ounce	30 g
4 ounces	115 g
8 ounces	225 g
12 ounces	340 g
16 ounces or 1 pound	455 g

10.4 Oven Temperatures

FAHRENHEIT	CELSIUS (APPROXIMATE)
250°F	120°C
300°F	150°C
325°F	165°C
350°F	180°C
375°F	190°C
400°F	200°C
425°F	220°C
450°F	230°C

CONCLUSION

According to the American Society of Metabolic and Bariatric Surgery, you can anticipate to lose at least 50% of your extra weight after gastric sleeve surgery in 18 to 24 months. Some people lose 60-70 percent of their body weight.

However, surgery alone is not sufficient for weight loss. Deliberate actions should be taken to keep off the weight after surgery. You have to be committed to following a specific diet plan, exercise regularly and stay motivated towards your goal. I encourage you to stay focused and follow the tips and guidelines in this book.

Enjoy your new life!

REFERENCES

Healthline Media. "Gastric Sleeve Diet." Accessed July 10, 2021. https://www.healthline.com/health/gastric-sleeve-diet

American Society for Metabolic and Bariatric Surgery. "FAQs Of Bariatric-Surgery | ASMBS." Accessed July 10, 2021. https://asmbs.org/patients/faqs-of-bariatric-surgery

Lightning Source UK Ltd.
Milton Keynes UK
UKHW051006021222
413181UK00010B/1441